Above and Beyond Cancer

To everyone whose life has been touched by cancer, especially those who have shared their personal stories in order to provide hope to others. Your courage and generosity of spirit have inspired this book.

Above and Beyond Cancer

Richard L. Deming, M.D.
Photography by Dylan Huey

Drake Community Press
Des Moines, Iowa

Other Books by the Drake Community Press
Zakery's Bridge: Children's Journeys from Around the World to Iowa (2011)
The Ones I Bring With Me/*Los que llevo conmigo* (2014)
A Spectrum of Faith: Religions of the World in America's Heartland (2017)

Published by
Drake Community Press
2507 University Avenue
Des Moines, Iowa 50311

All photography by Dylan Huey unless otherwise noted.
Printed and bound in the USA
Library of Congress Control Number: 2020903269
ISBN: 978-0-578-64892-7 (hardcover)
ISBN: 978-0-578-65199-6 (softcover)

Additional information can be found at
www.drakecommunitypress.org.

Table of Contents

Kilimanjaro

Foreword by Senator Tom Harkin (retired)

Some years ago I had heard about a cancer doctor in Des Moines who was taking patients on mountain climbing expeditions. I thought this was very interesting for several reasons. First, my wife and I in our younger years had done a number of climbs, including Mount Kilimanjaro where many of the vignettes in this book take place. Secondly, I was chairman of the Senate committee that funds medical research, including cancer research at the National Cancer Institute, and also chairman of the committee that sets health policy at the federal level. We had just passed the Affordable Care Act. Lastly, I am a cancer survivor of a different sort: four of my five siblings—two sisters and two brothers—died of cancer. Three left behind young families.

On the one hand, I was proud of my long support for more funding of biomedical research generally, and cancer research specifically, at the National Institutes of Health. On the other hand, I had long been curious about other approaches to medicine, to the "healing arts." During an official trip to China visiting hospitals, health centers, and pharmacies, non-allopathic approaches to healing and disease prevention became compelling. I started the Office of Alternative Medicine at the National Institutes of Health (then strenuously opposed by the majority of the scientific community), which is now the National Center for Integrative Health at the NIH.

I finally got to meet Dr. Deming. Over the last several years I have come to know him as a cancer doctor who will use whatever technology is called for in combating a patient's disease, and who also practices what he calls Narrative Medicine. Dr. Deming says this is "compassionate listening to the story of a patient's illness," in order to promote healing. It is fundamental integrative medicine as well! Medicine that takes into account the whole person and places great emphasis on the therapeutic relationship between doctor and patient.

You will see in this book that Dr. Deming is a true practitioner of the "Healing Arts." This is the practice of promoting healing, wellness, coping with cancer, and personal change that happens when one is confronted with a diagnosis of cancer. As Mary Gottschalk, one of the book's contributors, says, "Your life isn't over because you got cancer. It's just going to take a different path." It is Dr. Deming who helps his patients take that different path by inspiring them and challenging them to do things they thought impossible, like climbing a mountain!

There is wisdom and inspiration in these pages. The wisdom of Dr. Deming and the wisdom and insights of his patients as they conquer mountains and the disease of cancer. As one patient put it, "Combating cancer is like climbing a mountain, one step at a time." Or as patient Leah Dietrich says, "Facing our cancer has given us the courage to climb a mountain." And to quote Dr.

Deming from one of his narratives, "not all patients can be cured, but all patients can be healed." Which leads to this quote about the good doctor, again by Mary Gottschalk, "There is a miraculous quality about that man."

Although Dr. Deming is far too gracious and self-effacing to lay claim to being a "miracle man," his guidance, compassion and "narrative medicine" lead his patients to their own miraculous healing and acceptance of a "different path." Keep moving, this book tells us through its words and pictures. All you have to do is take the next step. You will come to realize in reading these narratives that the joy in living is determined by life's beauty but also by its struggles. You will be convinced, as I have become convinced through the years, that there is " something else" that contributes to the healing of patients and the cures wrought by modern technology. That "something else" is what this book is about.

Tibet

Introduction by Richard L. Deming, M.D.

On the evening of September 10, 2019, I stood on the steps of the Lincoln Memorial in Washington, D.C., looking out on the Reflecting Pool with the Washington Monument brightly illuminated in the near distance. There, at the very spot where Martin Luther King Jr. delivered his speech "I Have a Dream" in August 1963, I gathered my composure and approached the microphone to address the thousands assembled as part of the American Cancer Society Cancer Action Network Lobby Day.

It had been an invigorating day. Cancer survivors and caregivers from every congressional district in the country had come to D.C. for meetings with our senators and congressmen to advocate for public policy to advance cancer research, improve access to care and reduce the use of tobacco. At nightfall, 40,000 luminaries, each decorated in memory of someone living with cancer or someone who had died of cancer, glowed in shimmering silence around the Reflecting Pool. One of those paper lanterns bore the name Odetta Deming, my mom, who died of cancer in South Dakota in 1977 during my second year of medical school.

"I became a cancer doctor because of my mother," I said into the microphone and to the sea of faces before me. It wasn't easy to utter those words; somehow, I feared others would find it shallow or trite of me to link my career path to my mom's illness.

So, for years leading to that moment, whenever I was asked "What made you decide to become a cancer doctor?" I usually gave a long-winded answer describing my aptitude for math and science and my desire to be involved in a complex field of medicine that requires the use of right- and left-brain thinking, since caring for cancer patients requires attention to all aspects of a patient's being, including the physical, emotional, psychological, philosophical and spiritual dimensions.

The truth is that I had long been reluctant to acknowledge the role that my mom's life, death and illness played in my journey. But on this night, on this sacred spot where so much emotion has been expressed by so many individuals over the course of American history, it felt liberating to share that Odetta Deming was diagnosed with incurable cancer when I was a junior in high school and that she died at age 52. She never got to see me realize my goal, but I know she would be immensely proud of me. Her presence has been a guiding light on my path to becoming the doctor and person I am.

This book has been quietly forming for a long time. Just as I have acknowledged the role that my mom played in guiding me to the calling of an oncologist, I also acknowledge the gentle guiding hands of all my patients and their families. Caring for people with cancer is a humbling endeavor. Sir William Osler said, "The good physician treats the disease; the great physician treats the patient who has the disease."

Every patient has a story. Yes, the story includes the "hard science"—symptoms, CAT scans, PET scans, surgical procedures and the like. But fundamentally, the story is about the whole person, not just their illness. Hearing a patient's story requires an understanding of our human connection.

I remember the first time I was asked to speak at the funeral of a patient of mine. Carole was a lovely woman who was born about the same time as my mom, and, like my mom, had been diagnosed with lung cancer. During the course of her illness, she and I became close. Her cancer responded well to treatment at first, which gave Carole, her family and me reason to celebrate. But within a year, the cancer recurred. We faced the reality that her cancer was treatable but not curable.

Carole's husband and grown children trusted that I would be open and honest with them as her illness progressed. When she began receiving hospice care, I visited Carole and her family in their home. In retrospect, it's clear to me that the most important part of the care that I provided was honest information, authentic concern and unconditional compassion. Not long after that visit, Carole died peacefully at home with her family at her bedside.

When her husband and children asked me to speak at her funeral, I quickly said yes. But my answer did give me pause. Was I moving beyond appropriate boundaries? Would the family expect my involvement into the future? Would this set a precedent with other patients and families that I wouldn't have the time or emotional capacity to fulfill?

In the end, I'm glad I accepted the honor of speaking at Carole's funeral. As I reflected on the words I wanted to say about how she had lived her life and shared her love with others, I came to this conclusion: To find joy in our life, we just have to do three things every day. First, take time to see the beauty present in everything around us. Second, do something nice for somebody else. And third, let somebody do something nice for you. Since then, I have shared that simple agenda with many patients and families.

Twenty years after Carole's death, I was delighted when I ran into one of her daughters at an event in the community. The young woman introduced herself, gave me a hug and thanked me again for the care I had provided her mom. I told her how much I had loved her mom and cherished her memory.

Our lives are transformed by our human connections.

I have always wanted my patients to know that profound transformation was something they could choose, not just something that happened due to illness. In 2001, I participated in a Himalayan climbing expedition that I still count as one of the most transformative experiences of my life. Ten years later, I succeeded in my dream of bringing a group of my patients on what I describe as a mind-body-spirit journey to the Himalayan Mountains in Nepal.

For two weeks, 29 of us, ranging in age from 27 to 64, hiked to Everest Base Camp. What people may not know until they climb, however, is that a physical expedition of this magnitude requires an internal journey as well. Summiting a mountain brings people face-to-face with many of the concepts you'll find represented in the chapters of this book. Fear, suffering, courage, community, hope, joy, beauty, gratitude, compassion, spirituality and renewal.

In many ways, the climb recapitulates the cancer journey.

The storytelling and photography produced on the Everest Base Camp trip document a truly life-transforming experience. Basking in the afterglow of that first Everest journey, I felt inspired to form the survivorship organization Above + Beyond Cancer. At the time we didn't know that our stories of suffering or compassion or renewal would end up in a book like this. But now I know the power of storytelling. It has propelled me to incorporate the principles of narrative medicine into my professional practice.

When I first heard the term narrative medicine a few years back, it piqued my interest because I realized I had been practicing something very similar without knowing that such a concept existed. Narrative medicine is compassionate listening to the story of a patient's illness. In the process of sitting with a patient and actively listening, a true relationship begins to develop. I already knew that the field of medicine cannot fully encompass the concept of health. Not only are there social determinants of health, but there is a real

person and not just a patient who needs to be heard. As I developed my narrative medicine style, I also began to allow the reciprocity required of authentic encounter. This meant it was okay for me to share some of my own life experiences with patients. Doing so enhances my ability to help them heal.

Since that first journey to Everest Base Camp in 2011, survivors have climbed to the summit of Mount Kilimanjaro in Africa, Machu Picchu and the Andes Mountains of Peru, Mount Imja Tse in Nepal, the sacred Mount Kailash in Tibet and the Rocky Mountains of Colorado. Obviously, these mountain journeys have become a prominent part of many patients' lives, and their stories and photographs form a prominent part of this book. At the same time, this book is not about the organization, Above + Beyond Cancer or about any of the climbs. It is about the philosophical journeys that cancer survivors, caregivers and family members experience on the path through a diagnosis.

Steep and arduous ascents await you in these narratives. So do moments of bone-chilling self-encounter and despair, and moments of peace fragrant with stillness. Welcome to stories of bliss and blisters, stories of grit and awe and surrender. Welcome to journeys lived by people who know the profound impact of facing mortality square in the jaw. This book will take you to every dimension of what it means to be human and what it means to live in a world both fraught with suffering and lit with joy. No cancer diagnosis required.

Kilimanjaro

Cancerland

I shared my story less to recover what I had once been than to discover what I might be.

Arthur Frank,
The Wounded Storyteller

Nepal

understand our role in the world. One of cancer's most common metaphors is the battle against the disease. Who doesn't love a good fight with a ruthless enemy? The world is full of literature that compares living with cancer to a kind of military campaign including an opponent, strategy, weapons, warriors and, inevitably, victory or defeat. Unfortunately, every battle concludes with winners and losers. If you happen to be facing an incurable cancer, the war metaphor may not be the most comforting.

Everyone is entitled to their own metaphor. What metaphor might you choose?

I like to climb mountains. Many cancer survivors use the metaphor of climbing a mountain to describe their cancer experience. Like cancer, it's a challenge that requires our undivided attention. "Conquering the mountain" is a familiar phrase in the world of mountain climbing. But far from being the enemy, the mountain is like a partner or a friend on a journey of personal growth. It is our collaboration with this partner that enables our ascent. Sometimes the weather is bad, the winds are fierce and the snow is simply impassable. But when conditions are right, the mountain allows our summit. The steepness of the slope is not the enemy; rather, it provides the resistance we need to engage our own strength as we propel ourselves upward.

For me, cancer is like a mountain—large, unwieldy and sometimes treacherous. But we don't set out to destroy mountains. We climb them. How do we do this? One step at a time. It's simple, really. All you have to do is be willing to take that first step. And then one more step. And then another. No one can promise a climber the success of reaching the summit. Just like no one can promise a cancer patient a forever cure. What we can do is help people take one more step. And with that step, the journey has begun.

Who are you when you aren't paying attention to yourself? What stories do you tell yourself about who you are? Who are you when you introduce yourself to others?

No doubt about it, the three little words "You have cancer" have the power to transform the story of your life, the diagnosis rippling through the circle of your family and friends. But is your identity bound to the fact of a few abnormal cells lurking within your body?

Cancer is transformative, but it doesn't have to be a transformation to something worse. How can we incorporate a cancer diagnosis into our identity? And how does that identity affect our outlook on the world? Cancer survivors face such questions every day, along with decisions about treatment, dealing with the side effects of chemotherapy and radiation, the need to continue generating an income and the press of all of life's other responsibilities.

Often, we turn to metaphors—those phrases or images that allow us to relate to our experience by comparing it to something familiar—to help us

Nepal

The golden brown leaves in our cornfield rattled in the warm October breeze. They conveyed a sense of urgency, dry and spent from a summer of nourishing the ears of grain. It was 2008, and I was enjoying the first harvest season since retiring from the U.S. Department of Agriculture in my favorite spot: the buddy seat next to my husband in his combine. I loved watching the golden ears snap from their husks as the massive green machine lumbered down the rows. I loved the waxy feel of the freshly harvested kernels, the smell of corn and even the roar of the fans on the corn dryers. This is the time of year farmers anticipate most, the reward for their labor and investment. But I was feeling reluctant to take time for a mammogram and ultrasound. After all, my doctor and I were sure it was just another cyst.

Connie Duinink

After quite some time, the doctor was still writing in my file. When I commented on this, he told me that a lot of "doctoring" was doing just that—writing. I still thought it seemed excessive, so I joked, "Gee, what is it, cancer?" He paused and got a strange look on his face. "Well, your oncologist thinks it is." Don't ask the question if you are not prepared for the answer. I felt like I had been hit in the head with one of those swinging log jungle booby traps, the kind with all the spikes on it, swung from the treetops, knocking me to the end of the hall.

Jeff Lawrence

On the outside, I'm told that I appear a strong, victorious cancer survivor.... But on the inside, I'm trapped in "cancerland," consumed with fears of recurrence and death.

Tibet

On the outside, I'm told that I appear a strong, victorious cancer survivor. I go through the motions of my life, appearing "normal" in my various roles: wife, mother, friend, advocate, volunteer and nurse. But on the inside, I'm trapped in "cancerland," consumed with fears of recurrence and death, a lonely, isolated being.
Amy Colton

I tried so hard to be the all-American boy throughout high school and college. I gave up soda in high school when I realized it was bad for you. I gave up meat when I realized there was a backstory there. I tried to make every decision possible that would lead me toward a healthy life. I never smoked a cigarette. I literally felt as though, genetically speaking, I would probably live forever, and if not, it would probably be a car accident. Living life out loud was what was gonna get me. But cancer? Not on my radar.
Michael Zimmerman

Nine years ago I was diagnosed with an aggressive form of cancer which had rapidly reached stage IV before it was discovered. The origins of this Inflammatory Breast Cancer (IBC) remain a mystery. What is not a mystery to me is how the understanding of our experience of life from the inside-out has had such a profound impact on my uncommon survival thus far. I believe that while improved understanding of the connection between mind, body and health may be difficult to measure, the benefits are nonetheless irrefutable. Now when I catch myself caught up in fearful thinking about the past or worrying about what the future holds, I regularly dismiss its power to steer me away from the pure joy, love and health available in the present, and I accept my cancer journey as really *not* one of those "bad things" but merely the universe unfolding precisely as it was meant to.
Karla Hansen

My white blood cells are growing out of control, and my doctor says that almost one third of my chest above my diaphragm is being taken up by the tumor. My tumor. How do I fight myself? I have always focused on building myself up. How do I destroy these rogue cells that are really my own blood cells? I feel betrayed by my body. Who or what can I be mad at but myself? No one knows the cause of Hodgkin's disease. Smoking is linked to lung cancer. Eating fatty foods and not exercising is linked to other cancers. But no one knows what puts people at increased risk for Hodgkin's disease. According to my mom, my great uncle died from it, but doctors say it's not hereditary. Maybe it's good that I don't have to blame myself or my relatives for this illness. But if there are no known causes of Hodgkin's, then what can I do to prevent it? This idea is much scarier to me. I like to fight a known enemy. How can I fight what I don't know? How can I control what is uncontrollable? I'm going to have to become much more comfortable with the gray areas, with not knowing, with doing the best I can despite having only incomplete information. That includes whether or not I'm going to survive. I am not a gambling man, and the stakes are my life. If I could walk away from the table now I would. There would be skid marks as I peeled away in the parking lot, and I would never look back.
Andy Fleming

Right now, my biggest goal is to not die before I'm 40. I want there to be no brain cancer, and I want life to go on as normal. I want to go back to work and make decisions about work stuff. I want to go camping with my wife and my dog and decide whether to grill burgers or brats. I don't want to make decisions like this. I want to travel the world with my wife and my dog. I'd like to have some kids. I don't know, that's it.
Justin Anderson

Tibet

When your wig goes askew while dancing at your daughter's wedding, you're a survivor. When a new boyfriend comments on how perfect your hair always looks and you tell him that it's a wig and that you have cancer, you're a survivor. When your mother loses her struggle with lung cancer leaving you motherless and your children without a grandmother, you're a survivor. When your 11-year-old daughter asks, "Mom, are you going to die?" you're a survivor. When your body changes due to the cancer and its treatment, robbing you of your youth, your hands, your breasts or your manhood, and you get that cancer wants to take your confidence, your security, your invincibility, too—you're a survivor.
Leah Dietrich

I don't think of myself as a survivor. To me that has a melodramatic ring. I simply did what anyone would do—find good doctors and do what they told me to—which was to be cut, poisoned and burned, otherwise known as surgery, chemotherapy and radiation. Part of me remembers how nasty that was. Part of me feels like it happened to somebody else. After all, the brain, or maybe it's the spirit, has a wonderful amnesiac quality. That's why women who have gone through labor would even consider getting pregnant again.
Rebecca Christian Patience

Death doesn't know any particular person. I mean, it's not a respecter of any kind of person. And the same goes for cancer. Anybody gets cancer. It doesn't matter to cancer who you are.
Miriam Tyson

Being in shape was before the four kids, before grief from the loss of my parents, a miscarriage, a failed adoption and my brother's untimely death consumed me. Being in shape was before the stress of the twins being ill and in the hospital 13 times between the two of them during their first year of life. And it was definitely before my body had been ravaged by stage II lobular carcinoma of the right breast and a bilateral mastectomy, followed two weeks later by a lymph node dissection. Before six months of chemotherapy had taken my hair and my energy, and 33 sessions of radiation zapped what energy was left. The pounds started to add up. The side effects of the estrogen-stopping medication that had once fed my cancer didn't help matters. Nothing like being thrown into menopause to pack on a few extra pounds. Well, maybe a few is an understatement—try 60 pounds over the years. Despite all of this, something had been stirring in me since 2011, when I had completed all of my treatment and reconstruction surgery. I have overcome a lot in my 49 years. I've learned a lot and had many reasons to be grateful, too. But something was still missing. Something was still not right with my soul.
Diane Hammond

I'll keep using my cancer story to inspire people and make them laugh. Make them happy. They say that there's a good chance my cancer will come back and kill me, regardless of all the treatment I've had, regardless of how well I'm doing right now. I feel more prepared than ever to face that mountain, but I'm not betting on it, either. Cancer may kill me—just like anything else. It's just never, ever going to beat me.
Justin Anderson

Tibet

Nepal, Photo by John Richard

I was teaching middle school and a little seventh-grader said to me, "You have to read this book. It is the best book ever." So I read it and thought, *This is a crock.* This would not happen! This girl would not be experiencing chemo this way and cancer this way. And don't tell me nobody knew about her cancer. The whole town was in the dark about it, really? And then all of a sudden she's just dead? It was like cancer was nothing but a plot device. Well, I don't want to be a plot device. I don't want to be a stock character. I am not anyone's good-hearted cancer survivor girl, you know?
Kristi Meyer

I was missing my chemo port after it had been explanted. They have you take it home in a little jar, so it is kinda gross. Then I found out my kid had taken it to preschool and used it for show and tell. This absolutely cracked me up, I was laughing so hard. At the end of the school year, I was talking to the teacher and saying I had found the port in his backpack. "Yes, he brought it for show and tell," she said. "He was really proud of it and talked about how it gave his mommy her medicine." Oh, man. I would have loved to be a fly on the wall at that show and tell.
Cassity Gutierrez

From the very moment I was diagnosed, I told myself: You know what? For whatever reason this is part of your life path and you are meant to be on this journey. What are you going to learn from it? That's where it began for me. Every part of the journey was an opportunity to learn. That's why I knew I was supposed to go on this trip, that this was a spiritual mountain that I was going to trek around. I was going to go see how cancer is treated in a different country, too. I've always had this drive, always thought that I had to out-do myself. Now, when I look back I see those things aren't really all that important.
Kelly Schall as told to Steven Peralta

I am doing this for them—for the greater "them," to show them it is so important to end this disease that 41 of us are willing to travel halfway around the world and climb a mountain to prove it. I am doing this to show them that Above + Beyond Cancer offers life, love, joy and hope. I am doing this so they can remember it on the day when one of "them" becomes one of "us."
Cindy Torvik

When the doctor bluntly told Chris he would need a cord cell transplant or die, my normally very quiet and reserved brother, quite frankly, freaked out. We didn't understand why the doctors were requesting such a risky treatment and why certain tests had not been run earlier. Watching Chris pace the room more scared and anxious than I had ever seen him sent me back to my training as an English professor. "Let me get my laptop and let's just write some of this out," I told him. "You have a lot of good questions and I'm confused, too. Let's just write it all out and email the doctor." For me, writing helps clarify what I'm feeling. It was the only thing I could think of to do. Even writing a short story is in some way, at least for me, a way of understanding an experience. It might be my own, it might be someone else's, but the act of writing it down offers clarity and meaning. So, for a couple of hours, Chris paced and talked while I wrote down what he said. Together, we "workshopped" the letter, editing almost three full pages of text. The funny thing is, in the end, we never actually sent the doctor what we wrote. But that didn't matter. The mere act of writing it helped us find some peace, some clarity. And we decided not to go through with that particular treatment.
Yasmina Madden as told to
Allison Kaefring

Nick Vollmer

Why do you have to ask what type of cancer? People often ask this question first. Strangers in waiting rooms want to ask this first. They put it in a hierarchy and then decide, "That one's not so bad...."
Melisa Klimaszewski

Cancer smacks you upside the head. Turns your world completely upside down. At that point, it's up to you. Are you going to accept your disease and die? Or will you use it as an opportunity to develop deeper, more meaningful relationships with the people who share your world?
Justin Anderson

It's like when you buy a car and suddenly start to notice that car everywhere. You get cancer and suddenly every commercial, every halftime show, everything is about cancer. There's probably some sort of cancer ribbon for every day of the week.
Michael Zimmerman

Although we did not choose this role, we are the ones who serve as inspiration for those going through cancer. We are the ones who honor those who have not survived by living our lives fully, without a second wasted. We are the ones to tell our stories so that we may never forget that despite progress, there is much more to be done.
Amy Colton

Kathmandu

Nepal

It is the most unusual thing that's ever happened to me in my entire life. It's different. It requires a different perspective. Cancer requires a different kind of attitude than I think I've ever really known before. I feel very blessed that I've got a lot of good friends. I never knew how many good friends I had until it happened. The first thing that happened for me was a necessary readjustment of my thinking pattern.
Frank Owens

I didn't initially know their stories, but in many ways I already knew them and what they had been through. I understood their hopes for the future and their fears that cancer would someday return. And I had the utmost respect for them. In Nepal, as I reflected on my own struggle with cancer, it occurred to me that after my diagnosis and throughout my treatment the people that I wanted and needed to hear from most were survivors.
Michael Brick

Here's the deal, doc: if you were to set a pill on a table in front of me and tell me that taking it would allow me to wake up when all this is over without remembering a single thing but I'm still not supposed to take it, then I'd say you've got some convincing to do because I've got a lot of shitty days coming up. Cancer is an unbelievable education, like getting an acceptance letter to the best school on life. I'm going to put it in the signature line of my email: this is what I went through. I earned the degree, and that degree is survivor. Yes.
Michael Zimmerman

Whatever You Do, Don't Google It

It does not matter what you bear, but how you bear it.

Seneca

Kilimanjaro

Jill had a smile and warmth that melted my heart. She and her husband, Greg, were a happy couple with three small children and a world of promises ahead of them—until Jill's diagnosis of stage IV breast cancer. When I met with Jill and Greg to review options and formulate a treatment plan, I explained that her cancer was very treatable and that she would likely do very well with the cancer under control for a decade or more. But there was no cure.

Twenty years later, I can still feel the wrath of Jill's stare when I told her this news. She didn't fire me, but she said she was going to prove me wrong. "Nothing would delight me more," I told her. "I will be by your side from the start of this cancer journey to wherever it leads."

No matter how gentle and kind the messenger is, the message is a shock: "You have cancer." It's like being hit over the head with a two by four. Nearly every one of my patients remembers very clearly where they were and how they felt when they received their cancer diagnosis. Shock and stunned disbelief are among the first emotions they experience as they struggle to grasp all the ramifications of these three words. Then comes anger, for most. Anger at the diagnosis, anger at the messenger, anger at their doctor, anger at God. Why me? I didn't deserve this. Not my loved one; she's the best person I know.

Why does cancer wield such emotional power over us? It reminds us of two things we all know but try desperately to forget. First—we are going to die someday. Second—we don't know when that day will come. It may be a lot sooner than we think.

For 11 years, my relationships with Jill and Greg expanded and deepened, informed by the understanding of the sacred nature of being a cancer doctor. Our relationship, and the love, care and trust that it engendered, enriched Jill, her family and me with profound comfort and healing. Over the years, the ferocious anger her cancer initially elicited gradually transformed into acceptance. She chose to pour her energy into unconditional love for her family rather than be consumed by her contempt for the disease. Eleven years after that first meeting in my office, Jill died of her breast cancer. She lives on in the genes she has passed to her children and grandchildren. She lives on in memories she created. She continues to inspire this doctor to be honest and gentle with all who come to him for healing.

Fred Nelson

I was young and healthy when I was diagnosed with breast cancer. I went into surgery stage 0 but came out stage III. Before that, I was tossed aside by a taxi as I crossed the street on my way to a Broadway show, nullifying the strength and purpose of my spine. Life does not always go as expected. And I know that in the mountains, weather, altitude, illness and injury can disrupt the most carefully laid plans.
Julie Goodale

When I first got diagnosed, I didn't want to talk with people who had cancer because it was like salt in an open wound. I told myself to keep working, keep doing my job, and I felt like I would fall apart if I heard other people's stories. Slowly, that reaction changed, and now I sometimes find camaraderie in other people's stories.
Melisa Klimaszewski

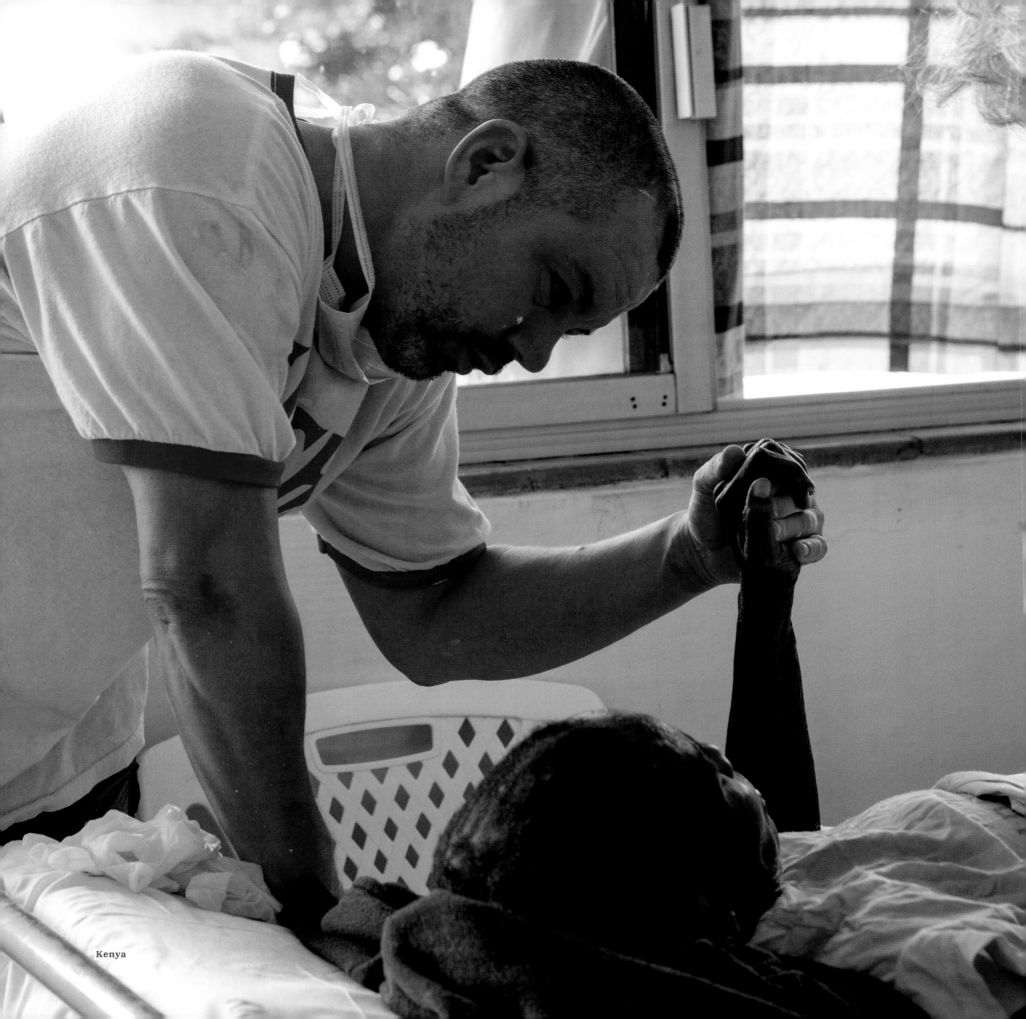

Kenya

The first time I told someone those most feared words "you have cancer" it was a guy who came in with typical symptoms: shortness of breath, cough, bloody sputum and weight loss. He was 56 years old and, of course, a smoker. His chest X-ray showed a large mass in his lung. Towards the end of the day, he and his wife inquired about what was known so far. I said he had a large mass in his lung, and that it was likely to be lung cancer. She asked if she could see the X-ray. She and I went into the little residents' workroom where there was an X-ray view box, and I put up the film. It looked like any other chest X-ray except for the giant snowball in his right lung. When she saw this, she completely broke down. The poor lady simply erupted in grief, sobbing hysterically in a way that made me feel quite helpless. This picture was telling her that her husband was not long for this world. She was inconsolable, red-faced and perspiring and hyperventilating. I told her we did not have a final answer yet, and that he would need to have a bronchoscopy to get a tissue biopsy to determine the diagnosis. But it did turn out to be cancer, and I believe he died in a matter of a few months.
Dr. Charlie Lozier

In the vast majority of cases, cancer is never anticipated, but arrives unexpectedly, like a thief breaking in to steal that which is most treasured—life itself.
Rev. Richard Graves

Tears begin to cloud my eyes. It's the beginning of winter and I'm staring outside into a cornfield with a light dusting of snow. I am 24 years old. I'm supposed to be living in a major city, going out on the town, meeting new people, discussing politics, work, food and sports. I'm supposed to be getting my career off the ground. I had been living a good life.
Andy Fleming

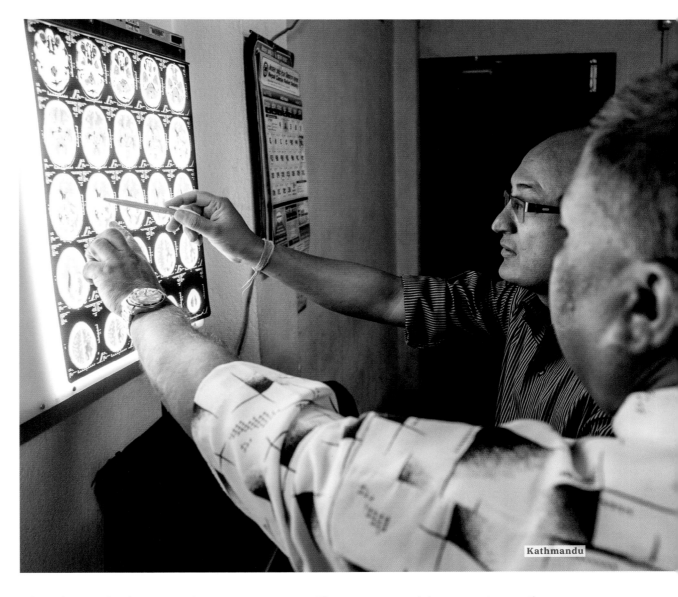

Kathmandu

I don't know why, but every time I go through major things that should be devastating, there is just a calmness around me. I don't just have a heart attack about it. I don't get very anxious. I don't know if it's my faith or my guardian angel or what, but I always seem to come through without getting too excited. Getting cancer just happened. Why am I any different than anyone else? I'm not. Lots of people get cancer. We don't always hear about it, because people don't talk about it, but a lot of people out there have cancer. It's about your frame of mind in how you plan to deal with the challenge.
Miriam Tyson

The surgeon read the report to me, then stared at the floor. His words swirled about my head. *Tumors, poor margins, necrosis, lymph nodes, sorry*. So, there would be no climbing in January. This surgeon—a father, with a picture on his desk of his son rock-climbing—asked me if I had children. I thought, wryly, that at least I wouldn't have to figure out how to explain this to them.
Julie Goodale

Colorado

That night my oncologist came to my room. "We think you have pancreatic cancer. Whatever you do, don't Google it. It is not pretty." I heard my wife, Susan, cry the cry of helpless sorrow. "Do you want to go home for the weekend?" I asked, standing behind her, arms wrapped around her. I could do nothing to keep her from this pain. I looked over into the dark window of the hospital room and saw our reflections, not looking at each other. All I could think to say that offered any hope was, "That's just one man's opinion." When we left the hospital, I felt like I was going home to have my last meal. I don't remember a lot of that weekend.
Jeff Lawrence

I remember thinking this would all be over soon and I could head home for dinner and a nice weekend. Then, in his monotone voice, the doctor said, "We'll have to take a sample and do a biopsy." He opened a drawer and pulled out an instrument that I couldn't see very well. Then he asked me to lean over the exam table. I did as he asked. He inserted the instrument, and I heard a loud snap. My head began to swirl, dizziness welled over me, and my legs grew limp. He had lanced my prostate gland. The room darkened as I slid slowly to the floor in a semi-conscious state. I lay there on the cold tile, my shorts and trousers puddled at my ankles, unable to move. The doctor covered my nakedness, and the nurse dampened a towel and pressed it against my forehead and face. Gradually I regained my strength, thankful for the cool towel, and readjusted to my surroundings. I pulled up my trousers and sat on the floor for a while as the dizziness dispelled.
Dave Bartemes

Kathmandu

When you've built yourself around the idea that you're never going to get knocked down and then you get hit with something, it hits like a ton of bricks. I can remember being downtown on Court Avenue one of the first nights after getting diagnosed and I remember seeing someone crossing the road with one of those Mega-Guzzlers. I had half a mind to just yell at them, "Why? Why me?" I was so mad that I had done everything right and that still it was me that was "chosen" by cancer.
Michael Zimmerman

Cancer is one of the great trap doors of life. When you are diagnosed with what is likely to be incurable cancer, you find yourself suddenly ungrounded, in free fall, plummeting down into the darkness. Or so it seemed to me a little more than one year ago as a young cancer specialist in Iowa City confirmed my initial diagnosis and likely prognosis. Cancer had put a real hitch in my hope.
Rev. Richard Graves

"Cancer." The word hung in the air as the world slowed to a stop. Cancer? Wait, I couldn't have cancer. Cancer happens to old people. Cancer happens in soap operas. Yeah, it happens, but not to me. Those few seconds felt like an eternity. Everything I had known in my 17 years came crashing down and shattered into a million tiny pieces as this dagger of reality pierced straight into my heart. All I could choke out past my waterfall of tears was, "I don't want to have cancer."
Kristin Sumbot

Kilimanjaro

I was just starting my senior year of high school and I found out I had Hodgkin's lymphoma, which I didn't know anything about. My parents had a set of encyclopedias, so I ran and grabbed one. It was from 1977 when I was just a year old, so when I looked up Hodgkin's it was this terrible, horrible death sentence giving me maybe six months to live. And I was like, "Oh my God." I was freaking out. I was just starting to apply to colleges. I was a senior in high school and just starting to feel like I knew who I was and where I was going. I was going to be somebody—until I started reading about Hodgkin's. That devastated me. Of course, after visiting with my doctors, they set me straight. There had been a lot of research and improvements of Hodgkin's treatments since 1977.

Kristi Meyer

Cancer? Never, not me. I am healthy, I exercise and eat properly. I am a fitness instructor, a mentor for others. No symptoms, just a routine mammogram only a month later than usual. But there it was— lines of calcification on the mammogram. Next, a biopsy, and then the truth: I am not untouchable. The roller coaster ride began: lumpectomy, followed by lymph node dissection surgery, hysterectomy, radiation. Doctors' appointments every week. Until: "I'll see you in three months." What? Who is supposed to check me? I'm on my own now? Reality sinks in: I really do have cancer and it sucks. I feel sick, sore, empty—why me? After five months of surgeries and treatment, I am just now accepting what I went through.

Bev Lund

Sometimes, I call Dr. Deming. He'll give me some Dr. Deming wisdom. Something he told me the second time I was diagnosed was, "You get 10 minutes a day to be angry and sad."

Justin Anderson

On my right breast, a dimple and small lump at three o'clock. How could that be? My mind raced as I tried to think logically. When was my last mammogram? Had I missed it this year? No, it was just this past June, wasn't it? Only three months previous. This couldn't be right. It could not be happening.

Diane Hammond

That night my oncologist came to my room. "We think you have pancreatic cancer. Whatever you do, don't Google it. It is not pretty." I heard my wife, Susan, cry the cry of helpless sorrow.

Nepal

Welcome to the Club

—

Thousands of candles can be lit from a single candle,
and the life of the candle will not be shortened.
Happiness never decreases by being shared.

Proverb

Kilimanjaro

"Hey, Doc, take a look at this." It was 5 a.m. on a June morning when my friend Bobby approached me before our regular morning work-out. Bobby, his sister, Debbie, and her husband, Scott, were part of our YMCA gang of work-out buddies. He pointed to a large lymph node in his left neck.

It turned out to be a nodal metastasis from stage IV tonsil cancer. The treatment was tough. Bobby received seven weeks of chemotherapy and radiation therapy. Even with a feeding tube, his muscular 220-pound frame withered to 180 pounds from the ravages of chemotherapy and radiation. He was hospitalized twice during his course of treatment, darn near dying of infection from his decimated immune system. Through it all, his family and the Y-rats were

by his side. They had given him a dozen goofy hats to wear during chemotherapy treatments. My favorite was the large green frog hat with four dangling legs just grazing his shoulders. And it became the favorite of the children of Nepal when, three years after Bobby was cured of his cancer, he joined the Above + Beyond Cancer team on the trek to Everest Base Camp.

I like to say that none of us is as good as all of us. In other words, there's not a single accomplishment that any one of us has achieved by ourselves that's worth a hill of beans. As a cancer center director, my goal is to surround every cancer patient with the support, expertise and compassion of a team of professionals who will help them create the best possible medical outcome. On this journey, the patient must take every step, but with support they can also discover their inherent strength.

Nearly everyone has heard of the concept of post-traumatic stress disorder. That's when the aftermath of extreme suffering or adversity leads to difficulties carrying out the normal functions of life. But there is an opposite concept I wish more people knew about: post-traumatic growth. When met with help and support, patients who have suffered extreme adversity can come through the difficulty with a greater sense of their own strength. Later, when that strength is tested, they may excel. They may even seek out adversity as a means to further develop strength and resilience.

Sometimes, as with a cancer diagnosis, adversity seems to drop from the sky. Other times, we might put a mountain in our own path and climb it all the way to the top just to prove that we can. Whether we are survivors and caregivers, on the mountain the labels fall away. We share the journey. We walk the same path. One day I may be strong and full of energy, able to lend a helping hand. The next day, I may be the one who needs that helping hand.

Kathmandu

In other eras, troubadours would sing ballads about these people. Traveling from town to town, they would sing of John, whose face turned black with pain; of the mighty Corey, who slayed his dragons as he ascended to the realm of the gods; of the fair Kerrie, whose love of her daughter carried her through. They would sing of Bev, the unstoppable; Sarah, the strong; Richard, the wise; and of the beautiful Madonna. Our own troubadour, Steve, would sing his tales to the sound of blues. It strikes me that, although we each have our own stories, we have been creating something new on this mountain—a whole that is somehow more than its parts.
Julie Goodale

Kilimanjaro

Tucked between two glaciers just shy of 15,000 feet was our first camp. I happened to be sitting right in the middle of the dinner tent next to its center door flap when Marcus lost consciousness. I bolted up, quickly assisting with the ties to the flap as people swept Marcus out of the tent for medical care. A crowd of doctors and nurses closed in, ordering me to elevate his feet, administering oxygen and yelling, "Marcus, Marcus, Marcus" over and over in an attempt to revive him. It was a scary moment. How would we be transported from these snowy peaks if he needed further care? Fortunately, thanks to the professional caregivers in our group, Marcus came to. Their cumulative effort saved him.
Scott Olmstead

Connections are not always poignant—there are a lot of silly moments, too. There were hour-long stretches where we played childish games, but it's all still about connection. Those moments of "would you rather" with a 24-year-old who had just graduated from college and a 74-year-old grandfather- were, for me, as important as the more serious exchanges. Sometimes it's serious, and other times, you know, we go low. But it really does feel like every moment of the day you're connecting with someone.
Yasmina Madden as told to Allison Kaefring

If our bond wasn't solid after supporting each other throughout a traumatic 10 years marked by cancer and the deaths of loved ones, we are forever bonded by simultaneously throwing up into trash cans.
Marilyn Vaughan

When we reached the summit, high in the African sky, I remember pulling a very large, neatly wrapped bag full of my flags out of my dusty backpack. It was almost time to display them. I began helping to thread a rope through each one, connecting them with hundreds of other flags to be strung from a glacier, cascading down in a sea of colors. After all the flags were hung, Dr. Deming gave a beautiful presentation and tribute to all who had been touched by cancer. We honored the memory of those lost, arm in arm, sharing tears and paying tribute to our heroes. I remember looking up, speechless at the sight of over 800 blue, red, white, green and yellow flags breathtakingly adorning the bright blue sky.
Jeanna Jones

I was surprised to learn how people in my age bracket deal with cancer, and all the different resources that are available to us. I feel like there's always a focus on childhood cancer, and there's more focus on older adults with cancer, but that middle range of people—I was surprised by how much I didn't know about them until I was one of them.
Jasmine Simpson

The day before we started our trek on the Kora, Dr. Deming asked me to give a blessing before a meal. This is something we all take turns doing and allows for a moment of reflection while also learning more about the people you are traveling with. It took me a little time to think about what I wanted to say, as I am not a religious person. What came to my mind was my unique relationship with the group as a photographer. I have a tendency to use my camera as a barrier between me and the world around. This can be necessary when I am taking photographs in the children's ward of a third-world hospital. It helps me do my job, which is to share stories through photography. But it can also be a wall that separates me from those around me. Everyone has a "wall" that they use to separate themselves when needed, but you can't leave it up forever. It's important to immerse yourself in what is going on around you. To listen to others' stories and share your own.
Dylan Huey

I want people to be aware that cancer can bring you together or tear you apart.
Michelle Flattery

I felt surrounded by wonderful people; men and women, deep and honest, open and loving. I heard no complaints, but rather, offers to help and share. Of course, it was tough, but we were in this together, and there is nothing like a shared experience to unite us.
Msgr. Frank Bognanno

Looking back at my own experience with cancer, I realize that the people I wanted to hear from most were survivors....I didn't initially know their stories, but in many ways, I already knew them.

Kenya

Bikal Adhikari

It was normal to have things not be normal. Our neighbors across the street had four children, and our families were like best friends. Their dad, John, had gone through cancer, chemo and radiation, just before I did. His was throat cancer. I could say, "Hey, guys, look at John. Mommy has cancer like John did, and now John is doing well." And my kids were, like, "Oh, okay!" Having just gone through it with John's family, cancer was almost normal in their world. The irony is six months after I got diagnosed, their mom got diagnosed with breast cancer and went through the chemo, radiation and surgery just like I had. So here we were in our little bubble, where their family was pointing back to our family and saying, "Look at Cassidy. She just went through cancer and now she is doing well." When I was starting radiation therapy, she was just starting her chemo. So I was close to the end of my hard year, probably eight or nine months after I was diagnosed. Our situation was unique because our kids went through it with other kids their age. To them, it was normal for their moms to wear a bandana and not have hair. I have this cute picture of both our boys wearing these cute bandanas in solidarity with their bald moms.
Cassidy Gutierrez

It is important to see that your neighbor, the person begging for money on the street, the person you're working with, they are all going through life, they all want to be happy, and any small part you can play in that is going to help them immensely. It will also bring you joy. My cancer journey and my journeys with Above + Beyond Cancer helped me to recognize that we are all on this earth together, something I believe is a key part of living life.
Jake Dehaai as told to Avery Melinsky

We share mass, we pray, we laugh, and there are tears. Homesickness and diarrhea creep into Lemosho camp overnight like a band of ninjas. We hug, console one another and pop diarrhea pills. Like 10-year-old boys, we giggle about "poopy" horrors of the night. I think of the lucky porter who drew the short straw and got to clean the essential, yet dreaded, portable tented commode.
Mary Van Heukelom

I learned to work within a team. I also learned that it's okay to surrender and let others help you take control of your life. Asking for help was something I had never done. These were people I just met, but it seemed like we had known each other for years. I was there for my teammates and they were there for me, unconditionally, no questions asked. We were able to laugh together, cry together and be vulnerable with one another. Yes, cancer was our common bond, but we had more in common than our cancer.
Bev Lund

Nepal

There we were, all together after trekking for four days, beholding one another with wonder and awe. It was such a spiritual place—Machu Picchu was thought to have been built as a sacred religious site for Inca leaders—and it kept me aware that I, too, was feeling more spiritual. So, what now, after such a profound experience? I reached out to the local Reform rabbi and shared my experience with him. He welcomed me back with open arms. I was on a spiritual journey, he told me. It would require time and baby steps. I've been going to temple on Friday evenings and attending an adult education series to relearn about my heritage as well. I find beauty in the cantor's songs and the speaking of Hebrew in the prayers. It hasn't been as strange on my tongue as I thought it would be. I think about how this change would have affected my mom, who passed away a couple of years ago. She would be proud of my newfound commitment, I know. And that's a comfort. At age 14, I had been part of a Jewish community of friends, but I began losing my connection to my Jewish faith. As I pushed away, I didn't realize I was losing my connection to a community as well. I've been away far too long. This is an opportunity to heal, to celebrate a return to my childhood home, to make things right again. I'd call this transformational.

Lorel Jeffries

Nepal

The physical challenge was not the only challenge on this journey. We also assumed the challenge of carrying the memories in the form of prayer flags for over a thousand other people who had battled cancer before us.
Scott Olmstead

I remember a survivor friend of my parents visiting me right after my diagnosis, embracing me and saying simply, "Welcome to the club." I am grateful for the ongoing support of other survivors, including those in Nepal. I know that I have an obligation to support others joining the club. Looking back at my own experience with cancer, I realize

that the people I wanted to hear from most were survivors. I have the utmost respect for them. I didn't initially know their stories, but in many ways, I already knew them. I understood their hopes and their fear for the future, that someday cancer could return.
Michael Brick

We all have our family baggage, but for most of my life, I had been number one. All notion of sublimating or putting aside what I wanted or my needs for someone else, the times I would do that were few and far between. I don't know if you would call it self-protective or whatever, but by the time Kent and I met, I had matured enough—of course, by

this time I was 65 years old, just getting out of adolescence—but I think I was mature enough to finally not be so self-protective. So the whole notion of putting more focus on other people, being more compassionate and more caring didn't come easily. But when I heard about the trip, when I heard there were going to be cancer patients and people whose job was to focus on those that needed help, I thought, *I have to do this*. I have to do this because I want to do this and I think it was placed in my path for a reason.
Mary Gottschalk as told to Graham Johnson

Nepal

I am not at ease in groups. I am more comfortable with one or two people, but I am rarely easy. Maybe that comes from a lifetime of letting my hands communicate for me. I am a musician. I create beauty or joy or despair by molding sound. Words are complicated, elusive. Language is fragile. I struggle to create order from 39 new names floating in my brain. I've never been particularly good with names, but now my memory for certain things has been scarred by "chemo brain," which was barely acknowledged 11 years ago when I first went through it. Even now, many doctors believe that it's just the stress of disease that makes us put the milk in the cupboard, head to work without our shoes or forget our sister's name. Unfortunately, some of us continue to suffer the effects many years later. Often my chemo brain takes the form of aphasia: I know in my head what I want to say, but the words get lost on their way to sound. The unexpected grand pause jolts me like an electric shock, as my brain is unable to restart the melody of words in my head. I try to hear the flow of the sounds, the rhythm of the syllables, like a musical phrase. We have three Gails and two Jims, one syllable each. At meals I look around to find the Gails—like I'm living inside "Where's Waldo?" I think of personal connections to aid my memory. *Steve, father of Jed, friend to Jim. Teresa, a mother, but not Mother Teresa. Tim, tall, not a Jim.* Daily, these people impress me, these climbers-who-are-not-climbers, who are not athletes. They suffer homesickness, illness, fear of heights, fear of their own frailty. But daily, they struggle forward in their red shirts. I climb with them, proudly dressed in red, their names now as familiar as household words. These are the stories I will tell of this mountain when I go home. Stories of my companions. Stories of struggle, of will, of breakdown, of triumph, of grace, and of acceptance. We few, we happy few, we band of brothers.
Julie Goodale

People Die Here

"For Courage"

Invoke the learning
Of every suffering
You have suffered.

A new confidence will come alive
To urge you toward higher ground
Where your imagination
Will learn to engage difficulty
As its most rewarding threshold!

John O'Donohue

Nepal

There's no darkness like night on the side of a mountain. Darkness isn't just present; it enwraps you in its relentless, almost suffocating, absence of light. I knew the 20,000-foot Himalayan peak called Imja Tse loomed above us, but the stinging wind caused tears to flash-freeze on our cheeks, and I'd long since lost feeling in my toes. It was easy to become separated from the group in the frigid dark since my meager headlamp illuminated nothing but my frozen breath.

Thank goodness for Ruth, a 65-year-old cancer survivor, who came into view, making her way forward under the watchful eye of our two climbing Sherpas. "There are two good things about being handicapped," said Ruth, whose left arm had been amputated as part of the surgery to treat her soft tissue sarcoma. "One is that I get great parking spots back home. Second is that I get two Sherpas to help me on this mountain climb!"

The closer we got to the cliff's edge, the more the trail zigged and zagged upward. "Be careful," our Sherpa warned us at a particularly treacherous point. "People die here."

That got our attention.

I'm not sure if there is really such a thing as fearlessness, but I do believe in courage. Courage is not the absence of fear; it's how we respond to it. We have to be able to say its name in the very presence of danger if we want to move forward.

Our Sherpa knew the danger that confronted us. He also knew the trail was passable and that focus and courage— Ruth's, mine and that of all us on that climb, including the Sherpa themselves— were required. With each successful encounter with fear, we learn that we have the ability to use it to navigate the path, no matter how dark, cold or treacherous. Over time, confidence builds, and courage can propel us to take on even bigger challenges in the future.

When I think of the courage required to face a difficult cancer diagnosis, many memorable patients come to mind. Take Justin. Just 27 years old when he was treated for brain cancer in 2009, Justin endured surgery, six weeks of radiation and six months of chemotherapy. For 10 years he lived free of the monster that had occupied a portion of his right temporal lobe.

Then out of the blue came a phone call from a doctor looking at his routine follow-up MRI scan. It was like standing at a cliff's edge on a frozen, toe-numbing night. Another surgery and now ongoing chemotherapy for an indefinite time and indefinite future. *Be careful. People die here.*

Justin is not fearless, but he is courageous. Recently, I took in a Willie Nelson concert in town with Justin and his wife, Alicia. Justin, himself an accomplished musician and composer, was invited on to the arena stage to be part of the group of back-up singers for the final song of the evening: "Will the Circle Be Unbroken." He could hardly believe his good fortune. He almost wasn't going to do it, but Alicia put her hand firmly on his shoulder. We watched as Justin mustered his courage once again and climbed the stairs to the stage.

Kilimanjaro

The phone call comes at 5:17 p.m. The surgeon is factual, concise and compassionate. It is stage IIIb melanoma. I'm going to need additional surgery. Appointments are set for me: the oncology surgeon, the oncologist. "Live each day fully," the oncologist says. "Take care." My heart is racing. My hands are clammy and I'm struggling for breath. I have no idea what to expect. Is panic what I should feel? I reach for my husband, who holds me tight. The dance begins.
Joni Livermore

One through-line in conversations about cancer has been that there has got to be an environmental cause. No one disagrees with this in a cancer waiting room, but no one there is putting money and time and energy into the causes of cancer due to environmental pollutants. Cancer is a natural cause of death. If I go, it's just my time to die.
Melisa Klimaszewski

Tibet

At the beginning of my cancer journey, I browsed through chat groups and decided to include myself in a cancer support group online. One woman wrote, "I am so scared of dying." I immediately eliminated myself from that group. I didn't want that.

Sanja Agic-Hajric

I don't know why I am so afraid, so unreasonably scared to death. At the airport, I say goodbye to my husband, but inside I'm screaming, "Don't let me go!" I tell him I am scared, but neither he nor anyone else knows that my stomach is a gnawing pit and that a vise grips my heart so hard I can't breathe. I want so badly to be excited, but I've never felt such overwhelming fear. *What in the world are you thinking?* I keep asking myself. *How do you*

think you're going to accomplish this? It's been weeks since I've been able to sleep through the night. Shouldn't they have given us some sort of fitness test as part of the application process? I would surely have failed it, and then I wouldn't have to be here at all. But here I am, about to fly halfway around the world to climb Africa's highest mountain.

Tammy Blaede

Someone suggested we sing a song for encouragement. The only song I could think of was "Spinning Wheel." I blurted out the lyrics "What goes up must come down." It was good for a few stress-reducing nervous laughs. But as I navigated the stone steps that led to the bridge, I felt completely exposed and uneasy. The footbridge itself was constructed of sturdy steel. The problem was you could see through the slats. Not good for a guy in my condition. I took a few steps forward, and the wind itself wrapped around me. Yikes. A little farther and the rushing water muted all other sounds except for my heart beating in my ears. I didn't dare look up because the view between the slats underfoot grew larger and larger, commanding intense focus. "You're doing it, John," fellow trekkers in front and back of me called cheerfully. "Almost there, John." To my pleasant surprise, I was able to lose my fixation with my feet now and again and recognize the support around me. "What goes up must come down," someone sang out loud. So there I was, making my way right through the fear and to the other side. Even the occasional bounce of the cables wasn't all that bad. That day, I crossed a suspension bridge on my own two feet, yet fully supported by these wonderful people.
John LaPrairie

When I was first going through cancer, I went three months without looking in a mirror—without looking into my own eyes. I just did not want to make that connection that this was really happening to me. I couldn't look at myself in the mirror for a long, long time.
Michael Zimmerman

Stephanie Stenberg

I had an aggressive tumor (some would say that fits my personality) that was detected early, so I think of myself as not so much afflicted as spared. I am not a cancer "victim" because breast cancer is frightfully common, and although I had no family history or risk factors, I am, as they say, of a certain age. Recently I lunched with a foursome of women contemporaries, all of us in our early 60s, three of us having gone through cancer. While I have eluded the eternal footman for now, the experience keeps prompting me to beg the big question: spared for what?
Rebecca Christian Patience

A couple of times,
my feet gave way. We
all were struggling....
One misstep could
cause us to fall to
our death. But I was
not ready to give up.
I didn't really know
how to give up.

Nepal

Kathmandu

We fly into terrain untouched by humankind, my eyes straining to adjust to a landscape I simply have no words for. I feel immense awe, an awe completely incompatible with fear. My thoughts stop racing. I can't say my breathing is normal, though, because what I see simply catches my breath over and over. At some points, you have to look up to see the tops of these mountains while also looking down at the clouds. The view runs off the page, so to speak. It's that immense. It goes on until it's just not there. Almost everything about the scenery is disproportionate to anything I've ever seen.
Suzanne Link

We begin our hike down to the waterfall. My first clue should be the hiking stick they hand us at the top. Worn smooth by use from the many hands before mine, this stick and the rickety handrail made of crooked branches become my lifeline. The steep steps carved into the hillside—some of them about the same height as my short legs—prove a bit of a challenge on the way down. When we finally reach the pool after our sweaty descent, I can take off my sandals and slip my feet into the cool water as mist from the waterfall refreshes us. A few photos and a short rest later, I decide to head back up with the first group leaving. Bad idea. My legs feel like Jell-O, and I can't catch my breath. Even some of the more experienced hikers are huffing and puffing their way up the steep incline. At the

top, I practically collapse on a picnic bench. Some people don't even break a sweat, which makes me pretty freaked out about my climbing abilities. That night, when I try to sleep, two prayers keep running through my head: *Lord, please give me that unexplainable peace I had when I went through treatment.* And this one: *I can do all things through Christ who strengthens me, I can do all things through Christ who strengthens me, I can do all things through Christ who strengthens me.* But no matter how many times I say it, it doesn't help. Fear has crawled in and taken over. The next morning, we ready ourselves to start up the mountain. I get back on the bus.
Tammy Blaede

Kenya

Tibet, Photo by Jake DeHaai

We were racing against time. If we wanted to continue on to the summit, we would have to reach Crampon Point before sunrise. We gave up our trekking poles to free up our hands to scale the rock wall. At one point, one of the Sherpas said to us, "This is a danger point. People die here, so be careful." These words rang over and over in my head. A couple of times, my feet gave way. We all were struggling. Annie and Judith questioned whether we should turn around. One misstep could cause us to fall to our death. But I was not ready to give up. I didn't really know how to give up. With the lingering hope that we would make it to the cut-off in time, we agreed to continue on until sunrise.
Julie Hamilton

"Her breathing seems so labored and painful," I remember telling the hospice worker during a care conference with my sister, Kristen, and our family. Before anyone else could respond, Kristen answered, "Hurts like hell, but if you don't do it, you die." It was the last thing I heard her say. She died five days later. On the mountain in Nepal, when I witnessed people struggling for breath at altitude, I remembered Kirsten's words: "Hurts like hell, but if you don't do it, you die." My little sister, my dear friend. For the life of me, I could not understand how something like cancer could happen to such a wonderful, bright, vibrant young woman and mother. At the time, I thought of cancer as evil.
Ruth Bachman

Courage is putting one foot in front of the other, even though you are afraid.
Joni Livermore

People love to tell you how brave you are and how courageous you are, and that's all great. People need to hear that. But there's this feeling that I didn't choose this. I'm just doing what I have to do. I'm doing nothing different than what you would do in this circumstance. We're no different, you and me. I'm just on the other side of the coin.
Michael Zimmerman

The Mountain Makes the Rules

You are a child of the universe,
no less than the trees and the stars;
you have a right to be here.
And whether or not it is clear to you,
no doubt the universe is unfolding
as it should.

"Desiderata" by Max Ehrmann

Nepal

I was riding my bicycle in a pace line with a group of riders training for an upcoming race, when, in a millisecond of unfortunate aerodynamics, the rider directly in front of me tapped the rear wheel of the rider in front of him. He went down immediately, launching me and my bike 23 mph into the air.

I woke in a hospital bed.

Friends say I landed on my head, blood seeping out of my shattered helmet and pooling on the asphalt highway. My bike helmet literally saved my life. I sustained a concussion, shattered my clavicle, fractured my scapula, broke 10 ribs, punctured my lung, and developed a hemopneumothorax and lung contusion. I spent five days in the ICU, seven more days on a regular ward and three days in an acute rehabilitation hospital.

Coming that close to dying was definitely a wake-up call. Although my accident wasn't nearly as significant as a cancer diagnosis, I consider it a kind of privilege that I got to experience the other side of the stethoscope, as it were.

The only problem was Mount Kailash.

For nearly a half-decade I had been planning a pilgrimage with cancer survivors to western Tibet, to what is considered the most sacred mountain in the world. Departure was in five short weeks, and I had already spent many of them fretting that I wouldn't recover in time. What if after months of planning and training and fund-raising I let everyone down?

Then I came to my senses. Thousands of comforting words and touches had flowed to me since the accident, buoying me with love and well wishes. Wasn't I blessed just to be alive? All would be well, I told myself. The coming weeks would unfold exactly as they should.

During my first few steps out of the ICU bed, everything hurt. But my job was to rely on others, just as others had relied on me. And that plan made me ready in time for the circumambulation of Mount Kailash.

Many former patients came to mind during my rehabilitation, but none more strongly than Kathy. In 2007, a malignant sarcoma on Kathy's left arm had returned. She needed more surgery, followed by radiation. Kathy already had neurofibromatosis, a genetic condition resulting in thousands of benign tumors throughout her body. She also had poor vision and an artificial knee, which meant a lack of balance and fear of heights. In other words, the perfect climbing partner!

On our climb to Everest Base Camp, Kathy fell down more times than I can count. But she got back up one more time than she fell. That's how she made it to the top.

In the eight years since Kathy's triumph, several more malignant tumors eventually left her with the use of only one arm. Despite her limitations, even a month before she died you would find Kathy enjoying the fellowship of weekly spin class at our cancer survivorship program. She inspired all of us to pedal harder.

Kilimanjaro

Chemo is what pulls your hair out. Chemo is what causes your tongue cells to regenerate and makes everything taste terrible. Chemo is what makes you burp all day every day. Chemo is what ruins your life. But it's also your best friend because it's your only chance against cancer. I realized that chemo and I are on the same team here, that it isn't poison, it's medicine. So I would go into the room and put my hands on the big bag that held all the little bags that held the chemo, and I would say this sort of séance prayer, something like, "I acknowledge that you are helping me and that you have to hurt me to help me. I'm with you."
Michael Zimmerman

We were sharing the stories of two grown men who had loved their wives and missed them terribly. For the first time, we had the opportunity to talk about our feelings surrounding the loss and our less-than-perfect roles in dealing with those losses. These feelings, long-buried in the crevices of our souls, were beginning to seep out. As we talked, this burden was finally out in the open. Caregiver's remorse, I called it. Tears welled up in our eyes.
Kent Zimmerman

But why hesitate? I know that men in locker rooms undress in plain view. I know that they walk to the showers naked as the day they were born—not nearly as pretty, but just as naked. I hesitate because I'm afraid they will know. I don't know how they will know, but somehow they will know. Someone may tell them that I'm part of a cancer group that's going to Kilimanjaro. Someone may notice that I slip a feminine pad into my shorts while I'm dressing. I need the pad because I drip, and when I exert myself, I spurt urine uncontrollably. They will figure it out, and they will know.
Dave Bartemes

We were quickly learning that we would need to accommodate the mountain, because the mountain makes the rules.

Kilimanjaro

Progress was based on the capacity of the slowest and most tired among us. Sometimes it was me. Sometimes it was Kent. Sometimes it was Brian. It didn't seem to matter. We were in this together, the three musketeers. And at every step, I noticed if Kent or Brian stumbled, if one of them needed an arm to lean on, if one of them was in need of a rest. As tired as I was, I slipped, almost without noticing, into the role of a caregiver. And, despite our fatigue, we seemed to have enough time and energy to notice the flowers and share our perspectives. It was, once again, a stark reminder of the lesson I had first learned so long ago but failed to apply. If you are locked into a set of expectations, however reasonable they may seem, the chance of disappointment is high. If you let go of your expectations, the opportunities for joy in the moment are almost infinite.
Mary Gottschalk

Mary, the fitness director for A+BC, was keeping an eye on me. She told me I needed to let her carry my backpack. It wasn't technically mine; I'd borrowed the backpack from my mountain-climbing brother-in-law, feeling instinctively that it represented my own share to carry. But Mary's words were kind and insistent. "Connie, this isn't the time to be a stubborn Dutchman." For several days I would start to weep whenever I thought of this—the first of many acts of kindness by caregivers and fellow cancer survivors.
Connie Duinink

And the machine gives the instructions to "breathe in, hold your breath, breathe," and it's not until someone tells you how long you can hold your breath for that you're like, "I can't breathe. I can't breathe." And then they stick you through this machine and you're like, "I'm dying, it's done."
Michael Zimmerman

Nepal

Things started to taste like metal, so food lost its appeal. All my clothes looked two sizes too big on my body. I'd wake up to find clumps of my long dark hair all over my pillow. My beaten-down body begged me for sleep, but insomnia kept me awake for long into the night. The hospital became my second home for days or weeks at a time. All the things that filled my schedule like exercise, friends and homework were gone. As the days got longer, my time felt as empty as I felt inside.
Kristin Sumbot

As I lay on the gurney and say goodbye to my family, I feel overcome by fear and grief. It feels unnatural and surreal, like it isn't really happening. I've barely had time to come to terms with my cancer diagnosis, and suddenly I'm about to undergo a major nine-hour surgery that will leave me missing one precious breast and reveal the true stage of the cancer. And I know this is only the first step in my fight. Depending on the results of this surgery, there will be more surgeries, chemotherapy and radiation. In the operating room, I desperately seek eye contact with the doctors and nurses surrounding me in their

surgical gowns and masks. They need to know I'm really one of them—a nurse, not just a patient. Instead, one of the nurses touches my arm and tells me that she's never seen anyone shake so much. Just before the anesthesia, I make a tearful, desperate attempt to make them see me as something more than a patient. "Before we start, I want everyone here to know how much I appreciate them. I know this is a long case, and I want you to know how thankful I am for this team." The room is silent. Then I go under.
Amy Colton

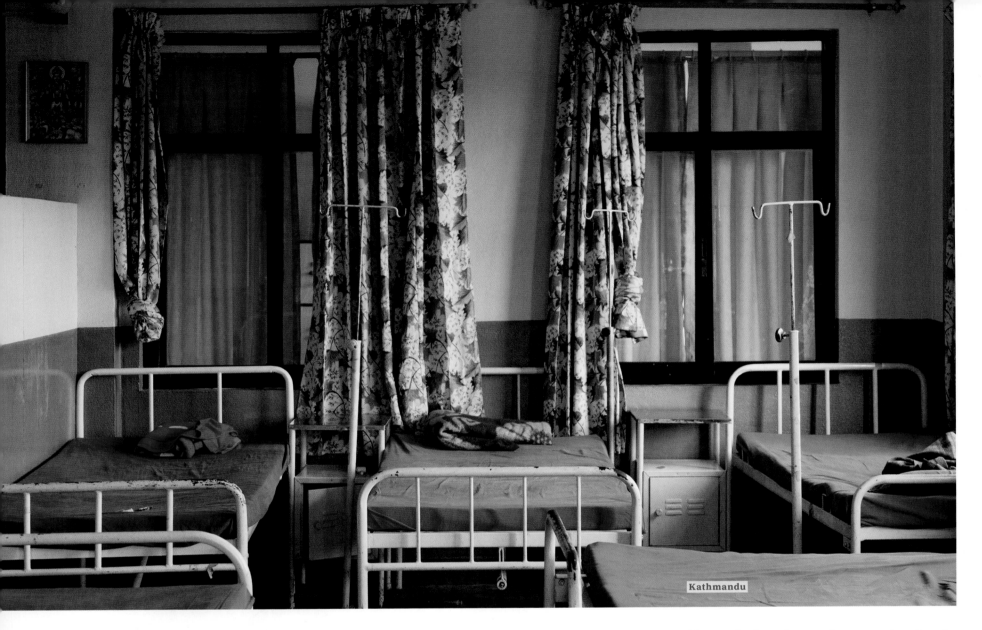

Kathmandu

When they told me I would undergo chemo for 12 weeks, I said, "You gotta be kidding. How am I gonna do that?" I thought about it, and I called Dr. Deming. And I think he was in the middle of something, but he took time out for me. "Well, you've got three options," he said. "One is, you do it. The next option is to find an alternative. Or the last one is, you don't do it." I remember that conversation very well. I remember the street I was driving down when he said that. "Well, I never thought of it that way," I remember saying. "Let me just think on that for a few more miles."

Miriam Tyson

For me, there's not really something I can't do. There's no distance that's too far because I've just gotta deal with the fact that it's a long distance. That's about it. I'm gonna get there eventually anyways, so I might as well just walk.

Michael Cuesta as told to Emilyn Crabbe

In my head I struggle. There are so many questions and decisions. Do I retire and enjoy life? How do I make myself better? Can I ever beat this? How do I stop the worry? How do I move forward? How do I plan? Do I need therapy? My mind is all over the place. I don't want to lose it, but I need something. My family is proud of me, pleased with reports, happy to see me moving forward. But they won't see what's in my head. I won't let them.

Joni Livermore

Change is the rule, not the exception. Small wonders happen every day. There's the kind we expect, like waking from sleep or the sun rising and setting, and there's the kind that surprise us, like a rainbow after a sudden thunderstorm. We look at these natural changes with a bit of awe at their existence. Then there are all the other changes that seem out of the natural rhythm of life—changes in our family and personal life, finances, employment, living conditions, health. When change occurs in our lives, we think we can control it, but the opposite is true. We can only control how we respond to change.

Ruth Bachman

I looked at the Sherpa, my hands on my knees, panting like an overheated yak. "I don't think I can do this." He candidly replied, "No, Mary, you can't." With that, I took leave to my tent. I said a prayer for those who continued the midnight summit as well as for those who, earlier in the trip, had been struck by illness or fatigue and turned back. Some had reached their limits earlier on and discovered that their journey hadn't brought them to where they had expected to be, either. I worried for them, knowing my own feeling of defeat, and hoped that they could find comfort in the realization that they had accomplished greatness, that a good book doesn't always have a tidy ending, that success is marked at all different heights. Of course, I was trying to convince myself of the very same things.

Mary LaPrairie

Every morning, before we began our trek, Dr. Deming led an exercise and meditation routine that included a reading from John O'Donohue, a Catholic priest and author of one of the loveliest books of poems you'll ever find. That book, *Bless This Space Between Us*, is a perfect metaphor for what happened to our relationship as Mary and I trekked up and down the mountain. But in Chunkung, at 15,500 feet, I reached my own personal "top." I was spent, suffering from emotional and physical fatigue. Along with another trekker, the 70-year-old Brian Fleming, and a very caring Sherpa named Pasang, Mary and I headed back down the mountain. It was a hard decision to quit, in no small measure because the key goal of my journey had been to wave a prayer flag for Anne in the winds of the 18,000-foot summit. I wasn't going to accomplish that, and it brought a profound sense of failure.

Kent Zimmerman

Dana Downing

If you have just been diagnosed with cancer, hanging onto your old life won't do you any good. You need to realize you are on a different journey. Reach out to the possibilities of that journey. Your life isn't over because you got cancer; it's just going to take a different path than you had planned.

Mary Gottschalk

You know, there are times in life when my experiences weren't so positive, but I'm blessed and fortunate, because I can look back on those moments and not hold grudges. I see them as learning experiences. You can get mad about something, but if you stop and think about it, there is something to be learned from all that happens. It shapes you into the person you are.

Miriam Tyson

Chemotherapy burns and scars my veins so they are hard to the touch. I lose interest in eating. In fact, just the smell of food invokes nausea. I can no longer be in the same room as Boca burgers and Brie cheese. Even the taste of water turns my stomach, and I didn't even think water had a taste. After three days of chemo in my veins, I lie down on the hard wooden floor because the ache in my bones will take the focus off of the nausea tying knots in my stomach. The nausea pill cost hundreds of dollars. Worthless. So much for the placebo effect. Even banging my head against the wall would be better than these days of nausea.

Andy Fleming

Kathmandu

When it came time to begin our climb at Imja Tse, I was in worse shape than ever. Six days of vomiting every meal had left me weak, severely dehydrated, even a bit delirious. I was in no shape to summit a 20,305-foot mountain. We set out in the dark just after midnight. Knowing I needed water and fuel that would be easy to digest, I ate a sports gel and drank some electrolytes. Neither of these stayed down. Farther up the trail, the lead group began to slip away from me. I knew it wasn't just them slipping away; my goal of getting to the top was slipping away, too. My determination was ever present, but my body couldn't do it. For the first time, I had to face the thought that determination might not be enough. Feelings of disappointment and failure flooded in.
Julie Hamilton

If she had to suffer, then I had to suffer, too. For me, being athletic was the best way I could find to do this. I've done some triathlons that take up most of the day, and it's painful. I wear a pink wristband in her honor every time, and when the going gets tough the thought of her picks me up and gets me going. Yes, it definitely honors her legacy. It's nothing compared to what she went through, but I try to suffer several times a month.
Dr. Jeff Nichols as told to
D'Azhane Felder-Johnson

To someone going through cancer, I say: embrace every moment. Find the good things in this experience. Find the adventure in it. Don't be afraid to have a little fun, but don't be afraid to bawl your eyes out like a baby from time to time. Just don't let it eat you up.
Justin Anderson

We were quickly learning that we would need to accommodate the mountain, because the mountain makes the rules.
Connie Duinink

They're worried that I won't make it to camp on my own. Did I want to ride the horse the rest of the way? No, I did not. No one else here needs to ride a horse. I didn't come all this way to ride a horse on the Salkantay Trail; I came to hike it. But then the guides tell me that I could be putting others in danger by refusing. I don't want to be a burden, and I definitely don't want to put others at risk, so I finally give in. As I pass my fellow teammates, they give me encouraging words, but all I can do is mumble about being a failure for having to ride the horse.
Diane Hammond

Nepal

Fresh Hell

_____

The truth is that things don't really get solved. They come together and they fall apart. Then they come together again and fall apart again. It's just like that. The healing comes from letting there be room for all of this to happen: room for grief, for relief, for misery, for joy.

Pema Chodron

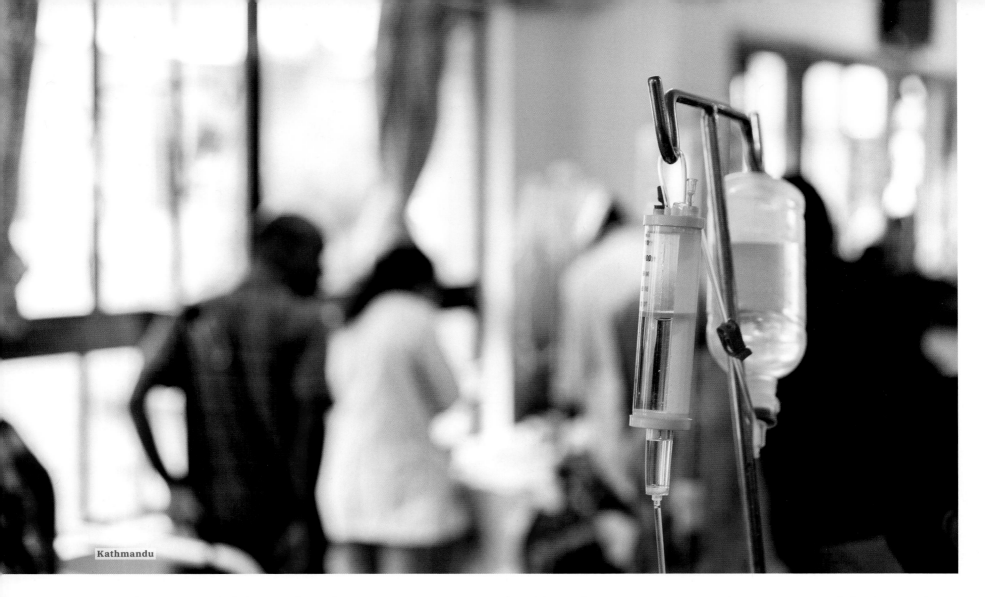

Kathmandu

When Kristi and I first met, she had just had a six-centimeter "anaplastic astrocytoma" removed from her right temporal lobe. This wasn't supposed to happen, especially at only 30 years old. Thirteen years earlier, Kristi had been diagnosed with stage II Hodgkin's lymphoma. She had already been through a cancer journey that included six months of chemotherapy, after which her doctors declared her cancer-free. She had paid her dues.

Unfortunately, being cured of one type of cancer does not "immunize" you against having a new cancer in the future. In fact, up to 5% of cancer survivors develop a new, unrelated cancer after their first illness. Kristi thought that all she had to worry about was the recurrence of her Hodgkin's lymphoma. Now she was facing a new and totally unrelated cancer. "Why me?" times two.

But Kristi was a bit older and wiser now. With a family of her own and a stimulating teaching career, she had more reasons to live than ever. So Kristi assembled her caregiving team, and we embarked on a journey that included six weeks of radiation treatment to the brain tumor site and six months of oral chemotherapy.

Kristi did more than survive; she thrived. She joined our cancer survivorship program and engaged in a regimen of healthy eating, rigorous exercise and lifelong learning. She went back to school and obtained a master's degree in English. Then she took on the challenge of becoming a contestant on "Jeopardy!"—and made it. Even having had part of her brain removed couldn't stop her from competing on national television.

Fast forward 11 years. By age 39, Kristi had enjoyed 23 lymphoma-free years and 11 years free of brain cancer. Then at a routine screening mammogram, lightning struck a third time. Breast cancer. Here we go again.

Over the years, I have developed a relationship of deep caring and trust with Kristi and her husband, Dan. With each cancer diagnosis, Kristi and her family have had to muster the strength and wisdom to learn all they can about her medical situation and move forward with hope and optimism. She and her family have been through anger, fear, worry, despair and determination many times over, with no guarantee of a bump-free future. Her equanimity has profoundly inspired me. Despite it all, Kristi has engaged with life in positive ways.

In one way or another, we will all fall down. And with the help of others, we will pick ourselves up. Not everything will be solved. Not everything can be repaired. But in our brokenness we can become grateful for the chance to learn what we're capable of.

Kilimanjaro

I have had more diagnoses than anyone else you may ever know, and I came through it all. I hide it well. It all started at age 17, when I was diagnosed with leukemia. There was chemo, radiation, a bone marrow transplant, pneumonia, shingles, infertility and Hepatitis C from all those blood transfusions. But no relapses of leukemia. I had kicked cancer's butt. I was strong enough to not just overcome cancer, but also all these other curve balls that being a cancer survivor had thrown at me. Then, in May 2011, 22 years after learning I had leukemia, I learned that I had cancer again, this time in the median nerve of my left arm. I went from doctor to doctor, each one with a different opinion on a course of treatment. This type of sarcoma was not responsive to chemo. The standard of care was amputation of my dominant arm. The next doctor would advocate just local resection of the tumor rather than amputation, but he couldn't guarantee that I would retain the function of my arm. Three surgeries and six weeks of radiation later, I lost the feeling in my first and second fingers along with a significant loss in range of motion. But I didn't lose my arm. During this time, an abdominal CT showed a suspicious mass in my liver. While I was not at risk of either primary or secondary cancer in my liver, doctors wanted to remove it. A fourth surgery removed the left-most part of my liver, which we then learned was a benign mass called an angiomyolipoma. After I finished treatment I decided to throw a party to celebrate the end of a very rough four months. A week prior to the party, I had a strange mole removed, which turned out to be a basal cell carcinoma, the "good" kind of skin cancer. Then, a month after my party, I found a lump in my breast. I was subsequently diagnosed with breast cancer in November 2011. This was my third cancer in six months, my fourth cancer. I was not yet 40 years old.
Cyndi Elias

Seriously? I'm really gonna do this again? But then I thought, okay, bring it.

Kilimanjaro

Incontinence may seem like a small thing to some people. Some might think I should do what I need to do and get on with it. I wish it were that simple. Incontinence can attack at any moment. All it takes is a move in the wrong direction, or a beautiful woman walking past. Sometimes sitting for a long period of time causes backup, so when you stand up, the security of the "pad" is demolished. I've had to race home many times just to change clothes. While the incontinence factor weighs every day, it is overshadowed by the "impotence" factor. It's hard enough to admit incontinence, but it's nigh on impossible to mention impotence. I couldn't help but notice that all of my physicians shy away from any discussion of it except in purely technical terms. They say it's a possibility. After surgery, after radiation and after hormone treatment, the subject only comes up if I bring it up.
Dave Bartemes

I am still taking medicine each day. I still have to go to the cancer center every month to get my implant. You still need to do it all, but it becomes less and less, and most of my life is not about cancer any more. But is there a day that I don't think about it? No. It's always there. But do I spend my time worrying? Not a chance. I'm really busy. To me, that is a beautiful place.
Cassidy Gutierrez

My friend, who has suffered through much worse than I have, has a favorite expression: "What fresh hell is this?" This is what I was thinking when I got diagnosed again. I was like, son of a bitch. Seriously? I'm really gonna do this again? But then I thought, okay, bring it. The world can throw some serious shit at you. There are times when you feel like everything is terrible and you listen to the news and it makes you feel so much worse. But really, there are so many other good things that you can see in the world and so much that you can see that makes it worth it.
Kristi Meyer

The waves crash hard for a while. And they hit every day. They hit and they hit, and then maybe a day or two will pass without them. And then you get to the point, maybe three or four months in, where it all becomes more routine, and this becomes your new reality.
Michael Zimmerman

I spent my weekends hiking in preparation for the trip. But I still had a high heart rate and moderately elevated blood pressure. In August I learned that I had mild cardiomyopathy, heart damage likely caused by a chemo drug I had received for leukemia. The cardiologist prescribed a beta-blocker and suggested another test that might help me decide whether or not to go to Machu Picchu. "Oh, I'm going," I told him. "There's no question." But what would Above + Beyond Cancer say if they knew? This was a trip for cancer survivors, not a trip for people with heart conditions. As the trip got closer, we had to complete the necessary paperwork. Had we ever been told we had a heart condition? Had doctors ever prescribed any medications for a heart condition? I feigned ignorance. After all, I hadn't known about this when I applied to go on the trip or when I learned I was selected. They weren't going to let me go if they found out. And that would not be fair. All this was going through my mind as I was hiking up the mountainside in Peru. It wasn't fair. Hadn't I had enough? I was sick of being strong. Emotions circled faster and faster like an erratic heartbeat inside my head until I couldn't breathe. I stopped. I couldn't hold back the tears. I was hyperventilating.
Cyndi Elias

In the mountains, when I was too tired to have any sense of time, I would play mental games with myself to keep moving up the mountain. *Walk until your steps fall out of rhythm. Climb to that rock where the raven sits. Don't think about quitting until you get to that next crevasse.* When my will failed even those games, I would listen to the crunch of my footfalls and count my steps. *I'll just climb eight more steps, then decide if I'll quit.* And even then, I persevered. *One, two, three, four*...That was what ran through my mind as I sat on the side of the bathtub, crying yet again. In the third week of radiation, I was too exhausted to continue, too tired to face another morning in a cold room, lying in my awkward plastic mold. Each night for more than a week I cried, convinced that this was the time that I could not go on. Each night I was sure that in the morning I could not return to the sad, dark room where children lay like corpses, where parents cowered in the hallway, where fear was tattooed on our bodies as they roasted from the inside out. Each night, tears burned my face. Then, each morning, I would decide to go just one more day. *One, two, three, four*....
Julie Goodale

I would have to admit that when "Breast Cancer Awareness Month" rolled around in October, I had a difficult time participating in events. Perhaps it was because that month for me was always full of visits to the doctor. It might also be due to the constant media attention given to breast cancer, which always seemed a little too in-your-face and my own experiences a little too recent. Besides, wearing a pink tee shirt or carrying a pink-ribboned grocery shopping bag just didn't do it for me. That seemed trivial; cancer is traumatic.
Connie Duinink

Tibet

I did the only thing I could think of doing: I began to pray. I chanted, letting the wind carry my voice up to the sky. I chanted as loudly as my lungs would let me, praying that Lord Shiva would recognize me as he had at Lake Manasarovar. I did not believe I had done anything so horrible in my life, but that was not up to me to decide. If Lord Shiva willed that I was not able to worship at Gaurikund, then I would have to accept it. With shaking fingers, I took my sixth match.

Bikal Adhikari as told to Robyn Michalec

The landscape turns brown and barren. Dust settles in my hair, the folds of my windbreaker, the lid of my canteen. I settle near the end of the group, marching pole to pole with "Bling Bling." Her nickname resembles her sparkling travel scarf, not her grounded spirit. She is a 42-year-old leukemia survivor, still undergoing oral chemotherapy. I hoist her daypack atop mine and encourage sips of water after each time she retches. I am not a cancer survivor; I am a caregiver. She moves off to the side of the trail arching her back, moaning softly. I wish I had a magic wand to wave over her and make the pain run away and the cancer disappear. I think of my own children when they're sick. Caregivers can feel powerless. We rely on faith, good doctors and hugs. After a tiny sip, we fall back into a slow rhythm, my boots, her boots. The sun sets upon arrival at Barafu Camp. Our tents, staked on a slope, slap fiercely in the wind. In the darkness, our feet slide along the loose volcanic sediment. Somewhere near, a fellow caregiver weeps from exhaustion.

Mary Van Heukelem

Dawn Taylor

I know I need to stay positive for myself and those around me, but for some reason I'm having a very difficult time faced with the realization that this cancer truly may be something I have to deal with for the rest of my life. That's where people like Dr. Deming come in. After our celebration of Kathy's life and legacy, we spent the night laughing and enjoying each other's company—just as Kathy would have liked. I remind myself that Kathy and Dick have been a part of my life, not in spite of cancer, but because of cancer.

Justin Anderson

As the air thins with each step, we step and say it out loud. Step, step, like the drip-drip-drip of the faucet. Just one more step. Cindy says it loud: "Come on, one more," and again, "one more." We are working as a team, comrades, making sure that every single one of us summits the mountain. With each footfall, time is ticking. We have confidence in each other's abilities, but the arduous day has made us weaker. Adversity is on our minds and in our daypacks.

Teresa Adams-Tomka

Nepal

Just because life seems to stop doesn't mean we have to stop living.
Kristin Sumbot

My tumor was Grade 4, Dr. Denis Clohisy informed me—the very highest grade, with very aggressive cancer cells. Still, my prognosis was "good" (40% to 65% survival rate) with a treatment package that included three rounds of chemotherapy, surgery and possibly more chemo. I asked him several questions, including: "What is the acceptable margin for resection?" This is another way of asking how much clear tissue they would need to take along with the tumor in order to feel they had gotten it all. With a look of gentle surprise, Denis answered, "2.5 centimeters—one inch all around." I knew that the cancer already consumed my wrist and so did he. After a rather long, pensive silence, I then asked, "What will happen if I do not accept amputation?" The smile drained from his face. "You will die," he answered. He urged me to accept the unimaginable, to choose life without my dominant left hand. Making that choice would mean accepting something life-altering, disfiguring and potentially life-saving but with no lifetime guarantee. Denis assured me that the goal of my treatment was to be cancer-free. I asked, "If I were your wife or mother, what would you want me to do?" He answered, "The difficult thing."
Ruth Bachman

I made it. I survived treatments, with love from friends and family. When it was time to return to my family cancer-free, I realized that their lives had continued while mine had been held back by cancer. I was still healing from the effects of treatments, a recovery that can take up to two years. But sometimes friends and family believe when treatments are done, you are done, too. That's not the case. You're still healing inside, physically and mentally. I wanted my family back, so I jumped in with both feet, trying to be mom and wife again. But during cancer, you change. You are scared, medicines change your moods, and you pray everyone around you is strong enough to hold on with you.

Michelle Flattery

My oncologist is Dr. Boros. I feel comfortable with him because we have a family connection—he treated my mother and aunt for breast cancer. Plus he says I remind him of his own son, Adam, who is about the same age as me. During our first meeting he performs a bone marrow biopsy right in the office. I trust him. Bone marrow biopsies are done to stage the cancer and see if it has invaded the bone marrow where blood cells are produced. I lie on the table, and he takes out what looks to be a six-inch needle that he fills with Novocaine. He says it will hurt like a big bee sting. He stabs the needle into my right hip above my butt cheek. Then he takes a scalpel and slices open my skin so that he can drill through my hip and into the middle of my bone to take a core sample of the marrow. I bury my face into the pillow, refusing to make a sound. For distraction, I imagine my friend Ethan, an Army ranger, who is deployed abroad being interrogated and tortured by Iraqis. I put myself in his place and refuse to say a thing to my torturers and not even give them the satisfaction of making a sound. The drill

Kathmandu

is reversed out of my bone, and Dr. Boros grabs a scalpel. He deftly uses the scalpel to dig out part of my bone to test. I stay quiet, so quiet that both he and the nurse ask if I'm okay. I can tell they are surprised and a little concerned that I'm not making a peep. "I'm okay," I tell Dr. Boros. "Good," he replies. "Now for the left side."

Andy Fleming

What does it really mean to be strong, and how important is it? Why was I so hard on myself for needing help that day, when I thought no less of my teammates when they needed help? We all needed help at times. We all had our difficulties. And often the person who had just needed help was now the one providing assistance to another person, myself included. Perhaps it's okay to let go, maybe just a little bit, and even embrace our vulnerabilities.

Cyndi Elias

Nothing but
Bright Blue Skies

Joy lies in the fight, in the attempt, in the suffering involved, not in the victory itself.

Mahatma Gandhi

Maryland

What has brought you the most joy since the last time I saw you?

This is the question I like to ask my patients when I see them, and it often takes them by surprise. Some patients might describe their children or grandchildren as their source of joy. Others may talk about enjoying time in nature. But sometimes patients can't come up with an answer. After all, they are going through a difficult time.

I tell these patients that pondering where they might find joy is the most important job they have. For those of us whose days are numbered—in the end, that means every one of us—there is no more important mission. That's because true joy isn't about selfish pleasure or the avoidance of pain.

"From now on, I will push past the fear of failure and of the unknown," wrote 49-year-old cancer survivor Karen Parman on the palm of her hand. We were on the flight home from Nepal after climbing to

Everest Base Camp with a group of other cancer survivors. Then she added, "And I will do hard things."

Every day of the trek, Karen was afraid she wouldn't make it to the top. She was sick and tired of being sick and tired. And cold. And unable to breathe. She hated living without electricity, hot water or toilets. She felt like she would do anything just to be back in clean clothes. Yet despite all of that, on the way back home Karen wrote in her journal in all capital letters:

I WOULD DO IT ALL OVER AGAIN IN A HEARTBEAT.

It turns out suffering runs right smack through the middle of joy.

Wait, you might be thinking, isn't joy sitting on a tropical beach somewhere with an umbrella drink in your hand? If you subscribe to hedonism, the attainment of pleasure and the avoidance of pain, that's one version of happiness.

But an entirely different version of happiness comes through finding

fulfillment in the attainment of self-realization. Aristotle called it *eudaimonia*. We seek a challenge that will help us grow, one like trekking up a mountain. No one wants to suffer, but suffering is ever-present in our lives. *I will do hard things.* That's why living a life that is overly concerned with eliminating suffering is not a path to joy.

"It was… the single most life-defining trip I could have ever taken," Karen wrote of her journey. "Without a doubt, the best gift ever!" You might say that through suffering Karen ran right smack into joy.

That's why I always leave the window open for joy, even when I talk with patients who have incurable cancer. In spite of all our medical knowledge or achievement, we physicians never truly know how well an individual patient will respond to treatment, nor how long they have to live. But no one can stop any of us, no matter what obstacles we may face, from keeping a daily lookout for sources of joy.

> The thing is, the night did end. We made it to the top of the mountain, we got a great picture and we got the hell off.

Nepal

When Lance Armstrong was diagnosed, a stranger sent him a letter: "It doesn't feel like it now, but we're the lucky ones." If you had given me the choice, I wouldn't have accepted cancer. But I didn't have a choice. So I woke up positive, proved myself a little bit, proved my optimism, proved my happiness. Now I've got this whole palette of colors to choose from that most people may never see. My days are saturated and vibrant. The thing is, the night did end. We made it to the top of the mountain, we got a great picture and we got the hell off.

Michael Zimmerman

I directed my energy not to negativity but to the future, dreaming about all the great things I could do with my life once cancer was behind me. Dreaming became my favorite pastime because looking to brighter days gave me the hope and determination to beat cancer and to move on.

Kristin Sumbot

Anyone with a score of six or more had 20 years less than what they should have expected. It really started with that, with knowing that I had a score of six and that my doctor said there was not a single exception out of 17,000 participants over a 15-year period. But I was really a healthy person. I mean, sincerely healthy. My mother is 88 and truly the picture of health. And I was the same way throughout the chapters of my life. I married. I had two fabulous kids, now 42 and 38. Those were good chapters, too. But I have to say that this third chapter, which you could call the cancer chapter, isn't really impacted by cancer. It's enriched by cancer, if that makes sense. This chapter is about being fully in the present moment and just allowing what's going to happen to happen.

Karla Hansen

Iowa

I struggled a lot with happiness during treatment, mostly because at first I just thought, "I'm just going to get through this. I'm crossing days off the calendar. Here's the start date, and here's the end date. Cross the days off." But looking back now, there were little things. My best friend from high school would come over and I would say, "Let's play Phase 10 and just hang out. You can stay as long as you want, and don't feel like you can't go— you can go. But for now let's just hang out and play Phase 10." I was reconnecting with her and with my family and all the people in my hometown that I hadn't really seen in five years. There were a lot of happy times when things were going well and we were kind of relearning each other and just laughing.

Jasmine Simpson

My goal, when I began this journey into one-handedness, was to be able to do, by myself, all that I had done before. I learned quickly that I had to prioritize what I wanted to maintain in my life and put forth the effort to learn to do lots of things over again and in a new way. For example, I was not interested in quick and easy solutions to my questions about dressing myself. Like Velcro shoes, elastic pants and jogging bras. Working with no fewer than 12 different occupational therapists before and after my surgery, I slowly but surely did the work necessary to learn to eat, write, shower, dress, put on make-up, cook, type, drive and live in my home. I was also determined to continue to pack my bags and travel independently to Italy or any other destination of my choosing.

Ruth Bachman

Sprinting towards that train, I felt completely in love with life. Here I was, racing with everything I had through the labyrinthine jungles of Peru, amazed at my ability to exceed what I knew myself capable of. This was more exhilarating than any action movie or studio sequence—this was real life! Real life is ridiculous, when you think about it. And thanks to those around me, its absurdity is memorable. We laugh together. We confide in one another. If, at the end of the day, you have a story and you have someone to tell it to, you're doing all right.

Joseph Sabroski

I was with my husband at the hotel right before my double mastectomy. We decided to send a text to our family: "Two boobs for sale. You only have one more hour to get them, so you better call now. We'll express ship them." My sister called me and said, "Yes, I'll take them now, please!" Some of it you just gotta laugh through. Dr. Deming and my team of doctors were probably the reason why I was able to use humor and celebrate every milestone I had.
Miriam Tyson

Maybe I will plant gentian this year in the garden. Despite having spent three months recovering from bruised bones and an inflamed tendon, my botanical tour to Tengboche in Nepal brings back pleasant memories. I am reminded of a difficult trip, culminating complex emotions and a once-in-a-lifetime experience with Above + Beyond Cancer. I know I'm not destined to climb mountains. But I will always stop and look at the flowers. And that's enough.
Marilyn Vaughan

Three in our group passed around a small guitar, taking turns singing beautiful tunes. When Joseph strummed a few notes, Brian and I shared a smile in recognition of a song I had mentioned to him earlier that day, one that had been so meaningful in my post-transplant rebirth. The line "This is the first day of my life" sweetly filled the air, transporting me back to that day I had finally been released from Mayo—my wife driving us home, my daughters in the back seat, and me with my eyes shut, wind rushing across my face. I stuck my hand through the car window, buffeted by the waves of air. Above us was nothing but bright blue skies.
Scott Olmstead

Nepal

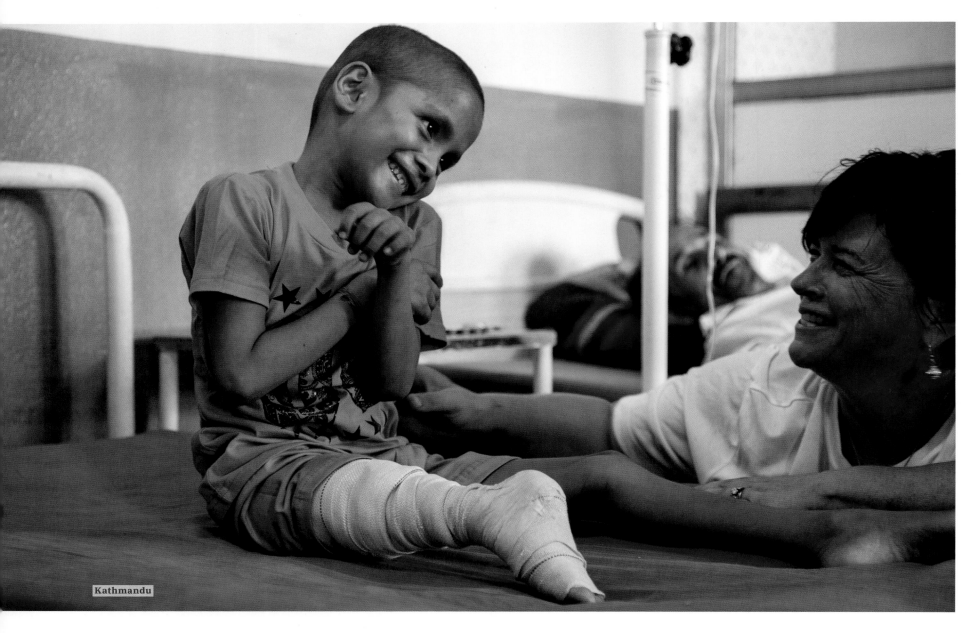

Kathmandu

We hike 20 minutes over a seemingly impassable muddy road to our first campsite. It feels like Christmas morning but without the comforts of home. If the team's smiles could be strung together like paper cut-outs, they would reach all the way back home to the United States.
Mary Van Heukelom

I did not need cancer to teach me to appreciate every day, but many people really want you to say that it's a good thing you got cancer because it taught you all of that stuff. People love this narrative. Cancer did not make me a better person; I was already a good enough person. I would rather have remained flawed.
Melisa Klimaszewski

The thought that this disease could take my life often occupies my mind. Yet I know my illness has allowed much goodness in my life as well. On this first day of our journey, I turn from thoughts of sickness, choosing instead to enjoy walking in the beauty of new friends and changing landscapes.
Judith Allen

When I first got diagnosed with cancer, my then-fiancée and I went on a honeymoon. We hadn't had a chance to get married yet, and I thought to myself, "I'm not missing this chance, I'm gonna do this now." Years have passed since then and we've probably been on twelve honeymoons by now, because we're still not missing any chances. You find your own reasoning. The sand is seeping through the hourglass, right? Even when you hold sand as tight as you can, it will still fall away.
Michael Zimmerman

I went by myself the first time I had chemo. People said, "What? You're driving by yourself between Waterloo and Des Moines?" But the doctor said I could. I didn't know what the big deal was, so I drove myself to chemo. I had this piece of lemon cake in my car. I had tasted this lemon cake while I was in the hospital, and it was the best ever. So I went in the night before, bought myself a piece of that cake and kept it in my car. Then after my first chemo treatment, I went right out to my car and ate that lemon cake. Girl, it was good!
Miriam Tyson

On our last morning together, the mountain seemed to smile its approval under brilliant sunshine and a cloudless blue sky. The guides who had taken such good care of us danced and sang as we thanked them for their hard work. I got one last picture with my tent mate, Annie, in all our grimy glory before our final trek down through beautiful wooded terrain. Though it may be strange, as I slept on a real bed that night, I dreamt I was maneuvering around rocks to get comfortable.
Connie Duinink

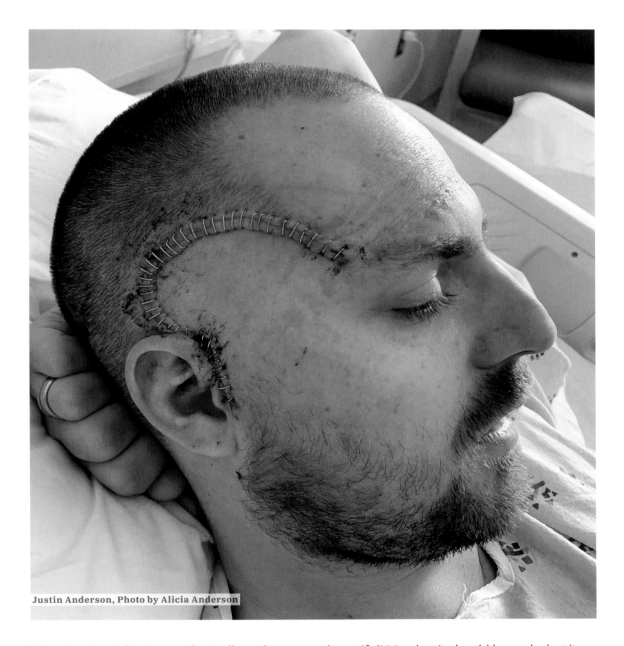
Justin Anderson, Photo by Alicia Anderson

There is a joy in letting go physically and living in this musical moment. I forget about looking silly in the eyes of my new friends, and I step, twirl, laugh and smile, panting in absolute joy. It's escape. On stage, we are a swirl of color, a collection of laughs and giggles, all with our own style. Some really know how to match their movements to the music, others don't, and I laugh at them, knowing it doesn't matter. Altogether, it's beautiful! It's what it should be and what it needs to be. Dancers and audience have bonded in this moment. When the dance is over, we bow, and I step off the stage to the smiles and applause of an amazing group of people. We are survivors. We are caregivers. We are one. May the dance continue.
Joni Livermore

Do You Have Homework Tonight?

The great lesson is that the sacred is in the ordinary, that it is to be found in one's daily life, in one's neighbors, friends, and family, in one's backyard.

Abraham Maslow

Des Moines

received four cycles of chemotherapy and then bilateral mastectomies. 33 radiation treatments followed, the last of them taking place that September. Throughout it all, Jeff and Madonna focused on their shared mission: Madonna's survival. Her illness had made it possible for them to fall in love all over again.

Once their cancer challenge was over, the couple decided to put a mountain squarely in their path. Jeff and Madonna joined me and 40 other cancer survivors and caregivers in January 2012, a year after Madonna's diagnosis, to climb to the summit of Mount Kilimanjaro. Although both were more athletic than most, Madonna's year of cancer treatment had reduced her strength and aerobic capacity. This became another opportunity for the couple to team up for a shared purpose. They made it to the top of the highest mountain in Africa and stood together in a passionate embrace.

On that cold January morning, they did not yet know that their biggest mountain was yet to be climbed.

In March 2014, Madonna's cancer returned, this time in her bones and lungs. The new normal would be learning to live with incurable cancer. The bond that this family shared on this journey made them all stronger. And on Easter Sunday, 2016, the loves of Madonna's life, Jeff and Jim, sat at her bedside and cradled her tenderly through the threshold to the other side.

January 2017, Uhuru point.

Pristine white glaciers surround me, gleaming in the African sun. Blue skies perfectly match the azure of the Tanzanian flag. I have carried a prayer flag that Jeff had made in Madonna's memory and some of her ashes back to the top of Mount Kilimanjaro where the couple had stood in 2012. Here at the roof of Africa are peace and calm and joy. I breathe in its beauty. I breathe out in gratitude.

This is a place one might consider spending eternity.

The patient is the one with the disease, but family members have their own journey when a loved one undergoes cancer. Complex feelings can arise on all sides. Perhaps a spouse recognizes the need to be strong and protective but must also deal with the emotional toll of a difficult diagnosis. Or the patient may feel guilty that the burden of caregiving often falls to family members. And when a child has cancer, parents may rail against how unjust it seems that cancer should happen to someone so young. Of course, the priorities of daily life keep coming. Budgeting, homemaking, work and schooling often

have to shift to accommodate illness. All of this can take a toll on families.

Still, I have been inspired by relationships that thrive despite a cancer diagnosis.

Jeff and Madonna are one such couple. They met at the hospital where they worked for many years—he, a doctor, and she, a nurse. In January 2011, not long after their son left for college, and anticipating enjoying the fruits of the life she and Jeff had built together, Madonna noticed a mass in her right breast. A mammogram, ultrasound and biopsy revealed aggressive triple negative invasive ductal breast cancer and positive lymph nodes in her axilla. Madonna

> They send you home with all this information—you know, pamphlets like "Dealing With Your Breast Cancer." So my daughter finds the brochure, right? And she says, "Do you guys want to tell me something?"

Tibet

My husband was no longer in love with me. He had taken another path and, once again, my life took an unexpected and frightening turn. I was in shock; I realized my children were, too. Ironically, the emotional and mental pain of this loss proved a far harder fight than cancer. That battle I had won, but I couldn't control the pain the kids were going through. It wasn't my body crumbling this time, it was our family. The divorce was a kind of cancer, the kind that had finally caught up to me. I reached out to a close friend of mine. She told me God makes the choice when it's no longer our time here. I went home that night and saw my three kids and understood it wasn't my time yet. That's why reaching the top of Machu Picchu meant so much to me. I would finally let go of the pain cancer had caused us, of the price that we paid—the dissolution of our marriage. I needed to mourn that loss. I needed to mourn the fact that I had fought to stay alive, afraid to lose all that I valued in life, only to lose it anyway, as a survivor.

Michelle Flattery

It has been one hell of a ride, and I've found myself in a lot of situations that I never thought I'd be in. Some really scary, some pretty funny. You don't really know awkward until your mother drives you to the doctor to give a semen sample. To top it off, when the nurse called my name, my mom stood up and said, "Well, how long does this whole thing take?" Definite face-palm. "I don't know, Mom," I told her, "but you're certainly not helping the situation!"
Charlie Cutler

Advice for someone who has a loved one going through cancer? Love them. Be patient with them. Don't give up on them.
Justin Anderson

My father passed away in 1998 from non-Hodgkin's lymphoma. I was devastated. He was the first person I had lost that I was really close to. Eventually, life got back to normal. Then three years later, my mom got Alzheimer's. When she was in the last stage of her disease, I got diagnosed with cancer. It was awful, but I have to admit that some things were hilarious. When I lost my hair to chemo, my mother had no idea why it was happening. She would laugh at me. Because it was my mom, I laughed, too, and sometimes it helped me forget my troubles. I brought her with me to choose a wig. Of course, she had no idea why I needed one. Later, though, she'd see my bald head and say, "Oh my gosh, put your wig back on! You look awful!" And we would laugh and laugh. We were both survivors.
Sanja Agic-Hajric

My wife, my mother—the people on my team, you know?—would sit with me in the waiting room as I waited for test results, and they'd start talking about whatever. Stuff like who was in the news. You know, just casual chit-chat. And here I am, waiting for the doctor to come out and give me the test results that could be devastating. It's a lot like crashing headlong into a T-intersection. These are the people closest to me, and yet I feel completely alone. That's where the cancer community comes in. They get it. When my family didn't get it, I would just whip out my phone and start texting cancer friends.
Michael Zimmerman

Nepal, Photo by John Richard

I remember being really sad and really scared at that moment, and it wasn't just because of what the doctors said, but because I could tell that my parents were really scared and that it was really hard for them to talk to me. I think as a child you are very attuned to that; at least I was. I wasn't really scared of my own diagnosis, but I could tell my mom and dad were scared. Some family friends of ours decided to hold a prayer circle for me. I remember looking up and seeing my father crying. He never cried. That was when the severity of the situation hit me.
Jake Dehaai as told to Avery Melinsky

During treatment there were a lot of unresolved tensions with my family about me coming out and being gay. My parents found out when I was a sophomore in high school, and it was pretty hard to even finish school after that. After graduation I just moved away, and we never really dealt with it or talked about it. So treatment kind of brought all those deep feelings about my parents and my sexuality to the front, especially because my partner at the time came with me to treatments. Both my partner and my parents had a lot of animosity toward each other, and there was just this vibe in the room like, "We're here for you, so we'll deal with all that other stuff later." Because I hadn't had those hard conversations with my parents about my

sexuality yet, it all just sort of compounded on top of having cancer, and it made me pretty angry about the whole situation. Like, not only am I a young person with cancer and I can't do the things other people my age get to do, but I also don't even know how my parents feel about me, and I don't know how to feel about this relationship.
Jasmine Simpson

I was part of a small group of hikers that kept a slow, steady pace up the mountain. I repeated the names of my grandchildren—Amy, Joel, Tatum, Amy, Joel, Tatum—over and over, matching my breath to the rhythm of my feet.
Ruth Bachman

Kathmandu

When I was told I had cancer, I remember telling my best friend, "I have a strong faith and confidence in what will happen to me if I lose my life to this." I choked back the tears. "But I don't want my kids to know what it is like to lose a parent at such young ages!" I told her, my voice cracking. "I don't want them to have to experience grief so early in their lives."
Diane Hammond

Many women worry about the possibility of breast cancer, but in my family the BRCA gene is hereditary. It was difficult to respond not only to diagnosis, but also to the probability that the cancer might come back, that the cancer required treatment, that the cancer might be passed on to my daughters, Olivia and Ella, and that the cancer had control over me.
Kelly Schall as told to Steven Peralta

I'm sitting with Frank in the Mayo Clinic waiting for yet another of the countless examinations, when I suddenly realize that this is no longer the place for him. Frank belongs home with his family, not drugged up in a hospital bed in some altered state. It's time to go home. "You can't do it," the nurses tell me. "He should stay here." But people telling me I can't do something has never stopped me before. I help a dazed Frank out to our car where I struggle to load him in, practically carrying him myself. On the drive back, Frank is so out of it that I worry I won't be able to leave the car even to go to the gas station in case he wanders off in an attempt to follow me. The drive is stressful. It's been several long weeks of very long days. When we finally make it home, I realize I have no idea how I'll get my husband into the house. I open the passenger door, and he practically falls out onto me. Struggling, I move him down the front walk, getting behind him to keep him upright and walking his legs with my own. The front door has never seemed so far away. All the while I'm limping along with Frank, I'm thinking the nurses were right. I shouldn't be doing this. The closer we get to the door, the heavier Frank feels. I'm about to let him fall from sheer exhaustion. Through the window, I see my 15-year-old son, Sam, napping on the living room couch. "Sam!" I call. "Get out here and help me!" But Sam is asleep. The only way to get Frank in the house is to lay him down. As gently as I can, I lay him back on the grass. Then I dash toward the front door, wake Sam, and we both rush back out to help Frank. I still think about how the nurses may have been right.
Vicki Bott as told to Zak Risken

This trip was the first time I was away without kids, work or any responsibilities. It gave me the opportunity to focus on myself, even if that was not my intention or inclination.
Dana Downing as told to Emily Wilson

Nepal, Photo by John Richard

We didn't really have a conversation about it. I was the only one who could step up at the time because my sister had kids, my brother had kids, my younger sister was only 17, and there I was, not doing much at all, just sitting out in California having a good time. I figured I had to go take care of her because nobody else was gonna do it.

Michael Cuesta as told to Emilyn Crabbe

They send you home with all this information—you know, pamphlets like "Dealing With Your Breast Cancer." So my daughter finds the brochure, right? And she says, "Do you guys want to tell me something?" All I can think of to say is, "Do you have homework tonight? This might take a while." It's really hard being a parent because you never know the right thing to say. You just do the best you can. It's been

two years. She has so much going on—high school, her own growing pains, that sort of thing. She never says she's worried about it. I don't know how much she thinks about it. Cancer does have an effect on the way you parent, though. You want to make sure they're okay. You just want to be there for your kid.

Kristi Meyer

Nepal, Photo by John Richard

I was more than a little apprehensive about becoming a grandmother for the first time 10 months after my surgery. A self-imposed narrow spot, brought on by worrying about diaper changing, playing patty cake and making French braids in a little girl's hair, had me totally focused on loss, on what I would have been able to do before losing my left hand rather than on what was possible to accomplish with the right hand that remained. However, I have been blessed by the discoveries my granddaughter, Amy, has brought to me. She was born with a thalamic brain hemorrhage and has compromised use of her right side. Together, we make a perfect pair of hands.
Ruth Bachman

I'm sitting in the airport waiting to cross to China, passing the time on my phone like everybody else. I'm scrolling through Facebook, getting updates on who is traveling, who is celebrating a big life event. Then something very peculiar happens. Frank, my husband, waves at me on Messenger. I am on this journey because of Frank, to preserve his memory and honor his accomplishments. Now we're about to embark, and my late husband waves at me on social media. I don't know what to think. At first, I don't tell anyone. I just sit there staring at the little yellow hand, thoroughly confused. After a while, I decide I'll just wave back. Just then, a Neil Young song starts up: "After the Gold Rush," one of Frank's favorites. But that's not just Frank's song—that's Frank.
Vicki Bott as told to Zak Risken

Another knock, more hesitant this time, awoke me. Dad sat on the edge of the bed while Mom cuddled up next to me, her head shaking slightly as it rested on my shoulder. "Hey, baby girl," they said. "How are you feeling?" I shrugged and replied, "Fine, I guess." I could feel Mom's tears on my sleeve as Dad pulled me in for a tight embrace. Something was wrong. Mom and Dad's firm and enduring manner seemed unstable. Plus, Mom never cried. Anxiety crept its way over me, and the air in the room started to feel thin. "We were at the doctor's office," Dad said. "You don't have mono." His bottom lip started to quiver as his eyes misted over. "You have cancer."
Kristin Sumbot

I always knew that I wanted to have children. Even back in college it was easier to imagine being a mother than being married. And I always imagined I'd have a daughter. But I kept putting it off. It was always something—a rocky career path, unstable relationships, or the next adventure awaiting me just around the corner. It always seemed like I had time. And through all the adventures and all the relationships, the daughter I imagined would call softly to me from the back of my dreams. Finally, it really was time to start a family; my spouse and I would try for our child right after I had just one more adventure. The Atacama was summoning me to Chile—to "Ojos del Salado," which means "Eyes of Salt." I pored over maps, estimating how many loads of food and water we could pack while climbing in the driest desert on the planet. Then, the subtlest change in the topography of my body interrupted the calculations.
Julie Goodale

The epiphany I had at the side of the mountain was twofold. First, I realized as a mother, that my life is not my own. My choices can severely impact others. Sure, I had made sacrifices for my children, but the sacrifices were usually trivial. They were missed sleep, a skipped run, a cancelled dinner party or a delayed promotion. They were conscious choices that I made to put the needs of my children above mine. But these choices had never interfered with my core being or my determination to reach a goal. I could always catch up on sleep another time, run another day, reschedule a dinner party or work harder next year for a promotion. But I would most likely never get another chance to summit Imja Tse. My ego, my perseverance to reach my goal no matter what the cost, could have cost me my life and rendered my children motherless.
Julie Hamilton

Nepal, Photo by John Richard

My mother, brother, sister and niece were coming to visit. It was Mother who insisted they make the trip, which should have been my wake-up call. Moms just know. How would I tell my family, my mother, my wife, that I had cancer? I was the oldest, the biggest, the strongest, smartest—afraid of nothing. Just thinking about their reaction brought tears. I don't think I've ever felt so helpless. I cried just thinking of their reaction. As soon as they walked into the room, I'd break down. I could not find the words, couldn't figure out how to make this all go away. Who could I stand up to or smack in the face? When they got there, we made chit-chat. I didn't say much. I was afraid I was going to crack. My oncologist walked in the room. It was as if he knew they would be there with lots of questions. He was upbeat, matter-of-fact in a good way. He explained everything to us. Now I really wasn't talking, due to the big knot in my throat. I couldn't stop blinking back tears. I swallowed hard to keep the sobs at bay. Or maybe to keep down a scream. I was trying with all my heart to seem strong. But moms just know.
Jeff Lawrence

Having cancer is often described as joining a great big family. In my case, that's true. Both my daughter and son have volunteered with Above + Beyond Cancer. In fact, my daughter has become so involved she even texts with team members to exchange inspiration and offer encouragement. Some of them even showed up to her high school graduation party, which I think is a great example of the way Above + Beyond brings people together.
Mary Van Heukelom as told to
Miranda Strelecki

They Weren't Going to Get What We Were Going to Get

Where you live should not determine whether you live, or whether you die.

Bono

Nepal, Photo by John Richard

In medical school, I learned a lot about the science and treatment of disease. But no one ever taught us about the host of social, psychological, economic and cultural factors that can affect our patients' medical care at every turn.

Take the case of my patient, Keesha, a loving and devoted single mother of two. At the age of 32, Keesha noticed a lump in her breast. When she sought care at a free clinic, they told her she would need a mammogram. And if she didn't want to get buried in medical bills, she had better apply for Medicaid first.

Keesha did obtain Medicaid coverage and found a physician. But every office visit meant asking for time off from her full-time job, arranging for transportation and finding reliable childcare. Each step in the process was hampered by delays. By the time I met Keesha, it had been almost four months since she first noticed the lump.

Her imaging made my heart sink: it showed a large tumor in her right breast and widespread tumors throughout her skeleton. Keesha's cancer was treatable, but those months had cost her the hope of a cure.

And then there is the rest of the world. During Above + Beyond Cancer's 2011 trek in the Himalayan Mountains, our team was led by Sherpa Lhakpa and his wife, Ang Lhakpa. As the only female Sherpa in our group, Ang Lhakpa took extra care to help our female cancer survivors. During our trip, we immersed ourselves in the culture and learned as much as we could about village life in the mountains. We noticed that there wasn't much in the way of organized medical care for the villagers inhabiting the region.

About a month after we returned to the United States, Lhakpa phoned. Because they worked in the travel industry, Ang Lhakpa had been able to get a blood test done in a small clinic that catered to westerners. The test revealed that she had an incurable form of leukemia. It could be controlled by medication, but the price tag was $80,000 a year.

I went to work on a solution for my friends. By arrangement with the drug manufacturer and a global NGO, we were able to arrange for Ang Lhakpa to receive the medicine. In 2017, five years after her diagnosis of incurable leukemia, Lhakpa and Ang Lhakpa met us in Kathmandu and became our Sherpas once again as we journeyed into the mountains.

Nearly 70% of the world's cancer deaths occur in countries unable to respond to the overwhelming challenges that cancer brings. Many people die of leukemia without anyone knowing what they had.

In the United States, medical advances have lowered the death rate from cancer by 26% in the last quarter century. But research demonstrates that racial and ethnic minorities and individuals of lower socioeconomic status have a greater incidence of cancer and are less likely to be diagnosed early or receive optimal treatment, compared with other groups.

Unfortunately, in our world today, where you live may determine if you live.

Kathmandu

A tour of the local cancer hospital left me with mixed emotions. The staff of the hospital was an educated group of individuals who worked tirelessly to bring what relief they could to their patients. In-depth conversations with the staff revealed their frustration with the extremely low cancer survival rates in Nepal. The equipment, medications and building they used were the decades-old cast-offs of more advanced treatment centers. Their efforts seemed pointless. Knowing this, caring people showed up every day to add even a small amount of time to the lives of their patients. I left the hospital feeling a need to fix the situation with bright paint, comfortable chairs to wait in, cheerful pictures on the wall and a good cleaning of the entire building. Would I be able to impart hope to my patients in an environment like this? Perhaps that hope doesn't really come from a building or equipment, but from the heart and soul that are present on the face of every doctor and nurse there. That's something no amount of money can buy.
Kelly Lamb

I had a family history of cancer and had regular checkups. I went to the doctor but was told everything was fine, other than my other health problems for which I was already taking multiple medications. Shortly after that visit I lost my job and my insurance. Additionally, I was in the midst of getting out of a bad relationship, and it was a recipe for disaster. Since I did not have insurance, I visited an organization that provides affordable health care and, while there, they discovered something that was not right and referred me to a specialist. There, they discovered I had cervical cancer. Again, with all of the other things going on in my life, being told I had cancer just made everything worse, especially the way I was told by the specialist.
Anonymous patient, interview with Christopher Roling

Nepal, Photo by John Richard

One of my favorite days in Cusco was the visit to the oncology office to meet one of just two oncologists in the entire city, Dr. Ramiro Tupayachi, who had used his own funds and family home to start his practice. As we got to know Dr. Tupayachi, we learned of the growing inequalities that cancer patients face in Peru due to the lack of equipment and services. There is no radiation equipment there, so patients are put on a six-month waiting list and have to travel 20 hours by car to Lima. As we explored more of the hospital, breast cancer survivors came out to greet us, dressed in traditional clothing and smiling from ear to ear. We sat with them and listened to their cancer stories. My tears flowed freely as I learned of the strength and bravery of the women. In that moment, there was no need for a translator. Vocal inflections and facial expressions told the real story. On that day, tears and heavy burdens were released as cancer survivors and caregivers across the world united for one cause.

Cyndi Mortenson

In rural communities they might have critical access hospitals, but resources are few. The majority of rural hospitals have closed due to a lack of funding. Therefore, one barrier is just the distance to a hospital. When I was growing up in a small farming community in northwest Iowa, my father endured cancer twice. We took him to Mayo Clinic for his surgery, but when his cancer recurred, he had to have radiation therapy every day for five weeks. That meant my father had to drive an hour and a half both ways just to get his treatment. Talk about added stress. On top of that, my father was a working man trying to support himself and his family while also paying his new medical bills.

Cassity Gutierrez

Kathmandu

I realized that these people were mirror images of myself. They were like us. They just wanted to get help for their child.

Nepal

Since returning home, I have become aware of the absence of treatment resources in this portion of the world. Not only in Nepal, but across the globe as well. In Africa, sometimes there are not enough medications to tranquilize the pain of those dying of cancer, let alone cure the disease. In addition, I learned that several types of cancer are common in developing countries but very rare in the United States.
Kathy Williams

These endeavors are important for many reasons, but most of all because cancer remains a threat to the world. Not just for the people sitting next to you. Not just for this community or this country. Everyone we encountered, from airline attendants to local Peruvian porters, understood our cause, explaining their connection to cancer as they designed their individual prayer flags to add to the collection that would move in the Andes air. We share an unfortunate commonality.
Brian Triplett

Being queer doesn't go away when you go through treatment. Looking back on it now, I wish I would've spoken up. "Hey, I'm feeling these feelings about where I'm at as a queer person with cancer, and I don't know what to do about it. I'm getting treatment, but I just need more help." I think I could have just asked for a little bit more help to identify that strained relationship between my sexuality and going through cancer.
Jasmine Simpson

The hallways of the hospital were packed with people, patients waiting for help and parents seeking aid for their children. Some visitors had walked for days from remote villages. You could tell from the laundry strung over doorways and guide rails that they had nowhere else to go. The hospital's resources were nothing compared to what I had grown accustomed to in the States. I struggle to recall even seeing IV drips in the rooms. In the ward, beds were lined up against each other, patients crammed into the smallest of spaces with their family crowded around them. But even witnessing what seemed as far removed from my own reality as possible, I realized that these people were mirror images of myself. They were like us. They just wanted to get help for their child. But they weren't going to get it. They weren't going to get what we would get.

Stefanie Stenberg as told to Ren Culliney

Patients' lives are put on hold while fighting health insurance companies for support, not knowing what their physical or financial future holds. Patients are forced to jump through administrative hoops to prove that treatment and tests are necessary, even though most of them have no expertise in the health care field. I was repeatedly denied coverage for a PET scan after finding abnormalities in my bone scan. Finally, my oncologist took matters into his own hands and called the health insurance company directly to confirm that this test was necessary for proper diagnosis and treatment.

Anonymous patient, interview with Krystal Kruse

Wendy Sanders

Being left out of clinical trials, such as those with mostly male or white participants, means medical breakthroughs don't necessarily apply to all. Certain diseases, treatments and drug side effects impact people differently by sex, race and ethnic background.

Lisa Esposito from "13 Ways Social Determinants Affect Health"

The treatment because of one my age, you know, I thought might be different. That is certainly a thought about the health care system, and I can't do much about it. Everything has to be approved by Medicare or I have to pay for it out of my pocket.

Frank Owens

You respond out of desperation. If he doesn't have a donor match, then maybe I can find one. It's crazy—like what are the chances that three or four bone marrow drives will find him a match? None, really. Regardless, maybe the drives collected 100 people into the registry who will be a match for someone down the line. If we are lucky, hopefully that includes people of color, as the majority of those drives were specifically targeting communities of Vietnamese, African-American and Latinx people who don't have a lot of representation in the registry.
Yasmina Madden as told to Allison Kaefring

Early in our trip, in Kathmandu, the group went to a cancer hospital in Bhakfabur, one of only two such hospitals in Nepal. It was clear that the staff there were very dedicated and passionate about saving their patients from dying of cancer and trying to prevent cancer in the rest of the population, but their facilities and resources were extremely limited. And, of course, most people in Nepal don't live near these treatment centers. They might travel on foot or ride a horse, but there is no car, bus or train to get them there.
Kathy Williams

Thank God that I came to America. With a diagnosis like mine, if I stayed in Bosnia, I wouldn't be alive today. Bosnia has good doctors, but they lack medicine and equipment. Somehow, it is as if all of my burdens have helped me to survive. For example, the war in Bosnia helped me to come here. Americans don't have any idea how it is to survive in a war without electricity and water. Even I find it hard to imagine. My husband lived for two years with no water when we were dating, as he was surrounded by the Sarajevo army. Eventually, I came to America, and then he came three years later. He lived through it all.
Sanja Agic-Hajric

There is a time for prescribed procedures. For example, if I were to break an arm, I would go directly to a doctor and have them do what is necessary, whether that is a cast or surgery, to make sure everything heals correctly. However, other health problems, such as gluten-related disorders, heart disease and cancer, need to have more individualized care as each of us has different genetics and we each react differently. This is not time for cookie cutter medicine.
Anonymous patient, interview with Christopher Roling

A substantial proportion of cancers can be prevented through healthy behaviors and access to cancer screenings and vaccines. Evidence shows that early detection of cancer through screening saves lives and reduces health care costs. Yet access to these services and the resources needed to prevent cancer are not equitably available, creating significant disparities in cancer outcomes.
Cancer Disparities: A Chartbook

God, Please Keep Your Cheek Especially Close

Think about it: it is easy to see God's beauty in a glorious sunset or in ocean waves crashing on a beach. But can you find the holiness in a struggle for life?

Harold S. Kushner

Tibet

It's ironic. I have met so many people who think that they want to live forever, but they don't have a clue what they want to do today to find joy for themselves, or to make the world a better place.

A cancer journey can invoke contemplation about life's big questions. "How have I lived my life? What have I done? What can I do?" For Plato, the bedrock for spirituality is the contemplation of death. In other words, the prospect of our own mortality makes us spiritual. For some, spirituality is defined in theological terms, by the name we give to our God. But it's a concept that is much more inclusive than religion, and it is based in impermanence—on the unspoken possibility of death's nearness.

During our first journey through Nepal, we had the opportunity to visit many temples and monasteries. We participated in prayer services and offerings, observed meditation and chanting, took part in the Jewish Day of Atonement and Yom Kippur, and received blessings from Buddhist and Hindu holy men and sacred prayer scarves from a Buddhist lama.

One bright October morning, Monsignor Frank Bognanno—we called him Father Frank—donned his white robe and purple stole. We set up a small table in the grass courtyard that did double-duty as a yak corral. Stone fences formed the boundaries of our "church," where we sought the presence of the divine beneath the sky's deep blue and the snow-covered mountains. Father Frank unfolded a Tibetan cloth embroidered with Buddhist symbols on a makeshift altar. Out came a bottle of Nepali wine and the aluminum water bottle from his backpack. The chalice and communion wafers were from home.

Father Frank, priest at Christ the King Catholic Church in Des Moines, is a survivor of prostate cancer and the oldest member of the Above + Beyond Cancer team. He is probably the fittest 72-year-old I know. Joining our team was Rev. Richard Graves, a 62-year-old Episcopal minister from Fort Dodge. He was cured of his testicular cancer many years ago, but his prostate cancer journey has taken a more circuitous route. He is still undergoing treatment for what is likely incurable cancer.

Father Frank offered Mass, and Rev. Richard read selections from Scripture. Everyone joined in the part of the Mass where we show a sign of peace to those around us. That part took quite a while as all 36 of us took turns hugging each and every teammate in a display of affection. During the sermon, Father Frank spoke about St. Thomas Aquinas, who believed that *vestigia dei*—footprints of God—are everywhere in nature. In the beautiful mountains of the High Himalayas, we saw many footprints.

Joe Bott

You go to church every weekend and you hear about the all-loving, all-merciful God. But then you watch someone you love die a slow, painful death. It makes you question those things. What loving merciful God? That was hard for me to swallow. I was pretty mad at God for a while. I still don't understand.
Dr. Jeff Nichols as told to
D'Azhane Felder-Johnson

I think my doctor was a woman of faith, a doctor of faith, though she didn't push it on you or anything. But she told me that the Holy Spirit called her to play a song for me. It was "God on the Mount." And every time I think about that song, I get the shivers. We have to thank God for when we're in the valley, and we have to thank God for when we're on the mountain.
Miriam Tyson

The prayer flag is about a way of releasing the spirit into the universe or returning it back to the universe.
Mary Gottschalk

I've always known life to be a journey, but a journey to where, you know? It's not about a final destination so much as it is enjoying the journey you're on. Being able to have fun, frolic a little on occasion, just to feel good. That's been very important to me. I have a different sort of a background. I'm the first person in the history of my family to ever graduate from college—the first person in the history of my family.
Frank Owens

The power I felt
was not just in
me. It was in the
mountain, the lake,
the trail and the
air. It embraced
the entire world
around me.

Nepal, Photo by John Richard

Far above me, Lord Shiva's home opened. The stone staircases led somewhere beyond the clouds; they led directly to the release of ignorance. The pressure of planning the trip, of keeping the team safe, dissolved. The power I felt was not just in me. It was in the mountain, the lake, the trail and the air. It embraced the entire world around me. Mount Kailash stood in sharp contrast to the blue sky above. The snow met the sky with a piercing distinction—it was the place where the earth neared the cosmos, where Shiva lived, where the power originated, felt by every member on the team, Hindu or not.

Bikal Adhikari as told to Robyn Michalec

Doing something as extraordinary as climbing Mount Kilimanjaro would surely give me opportunities to encourage others by telling about God's faithfulness during my experience with cancer. There were some people I simply wanted to "take with me" to the top of the mountain. Many of my family and friends had shared my difficult journey through cancer treatment with their love, prayers and encouragement. Many I cared about had faced that difficult journey themselves, and some had lost the battle. It seemed the climb would be a way to honor them in return.

Connie Duinink

We were here in Des Moines when we found out the diagnosis. It was ALS, or Lou Gehrig's disease. John's speech had already been a little bit affected. On the way home, he said, "I want to go to shursh," and my first thought was *Yes, exactly.* That's where we should go. We should go to church. Kneeling beside each other in front of the Blessed Sacrament, John's first words after he found out he had ALS were, "This is not fair to you." I replied, "It's not fair to you, either. Life is not fair."

Jo Kay Boyle as told to Abdullahi Salim

I have found meditation to be an extraordinary adventure. When I first learned to meditate, I was taught to stay in the present rather than daydream about the past or worry about the future. In meditation, I observe my inner landscape in much the way I observed and explored landscapes of Nepal. It is an intimate experience of learning about my own mind; in part, of learning how quickly and easily I get caught up in the past or the future. Perhaps all along my dream has been telling me to stay rooted in the present. This is more difficult to do than it might seem. Staying in the present can be difficult when I find myself thinking about the implications of this cancer for my life.

Judith Allen

I sat and listened intently to the story behind each person's flag, sensing the pain they carried. Often, before they left their flag in my possession, they would kiss it and wish it well, wishing I and the flag a safe journey and return home. Total strangers were praying for me and my safety. I found that enormously comforting. If the flags arrived in the mail, a note or letter often accompanied them, once again sharing the story behind the flag. I found myself sitting in my living room, reading the stories over and over with tears running down my face. I began to realize how sacred these flags were. I vowed not to let them out of my sight. As I made the long trip to Tanzania, I often smiled at my overstuffed backpack, knowing that all of my flags were safe and sound in my possession.

Jeanna Jones

Kathmandu

I wonder if I have lived a life worth living, in the sense that I have done good things for others. Have I been kind? Do people appreciate being around me? Have I made them laugh? Have I done anything of importance, anything to make things better? While my resumé looks good on paper, I realize at a deep, personal level that I am lacking. I have not accomplished anything that will leave a long-lasting impact, and I'm not connecting with people on a deeply emotional level. I can be so much more. This is something I file away in my head.
Andy Fleming

A couple of miles into our first hike on the Kora around Mount Kailash we came across a group of five pilgrims. Three of them were on the ground, and I think two family members were there for support, carrying food and water and supplies. It's just powerful. It's humbling to see what true devotion looks like up close. You know, you come up from behind these people, and they're literally on their belly reciting their sacred mantra and they do that over and over and over again. It's 33 miles around this path, and it took us three days. It's going to take them, on average, three weeks. You don't see devotion like that up close and personal without feeling humbled.
Dr. Jeff Nichols as told to D'Azhane Felder-Johnson

Sitting under a sky heavily sprinkled with glittering stars, I found myself contemplating the enormity of our planet and the heavens above. The cold night bit at my bones, but I refused to go inside just yet. I was listening to nature and feeling closer to it than I had in years. The wind spoke to me, simultaneously soothing and exciting. The stars looked like diamonds, not like the balls of fire we understand them to be. I marveled at the reality that someone like me, who started life in a small town in Arkansas, was resting this night atop the Kora of the holiest mountain in the world, Mount Kailash.
Jo Kay Boyle as told to Abdullahi Salim

I listen to the gentle nocturne playing outside my tent as I lie snuggled in my sleeping bag. Crickets; a stream gurgling; men lying in tents, giggling softly like seven-year-olds inside their living room fort; the lilt of Swahili and Chaga coming from the porters' tents; the odd electronic whir of cameras and computers being charged by solar batteries in the photographer's tent next door. All the quietude, punctuated by occasional belches and farts.
Julie Goodale

Prior to cancer I had lived a charmed life. I was happy. Optimistic. And I've gotten some flack from friends because they would say quietly to each other, "Of course you're happy. Everything goes your way. The world is giving you unicorns and rainbows all the time." And I remember thinking this is my chance. I remember telling Dr. Deming that this was my proving ground. This is my chance to show that this is actually who I am.
Michael Zimmerman

The spiritual part of the trek continues to inspire me to live with the "heart of a servant" and to live simply with the resources I have.
Linda Hoskins

Father Frank, a cancer survivor and Catholic priest from Des Moines, sat beside me on the flight from Detroit to Amsterdam, so he knows how real the fear of flying is for me. He'd prayed before that flight, saying, "And God, please keep your cheek especially close to Suzanne's." He asks now if I'd like him to sit beside me as he's in the process of switching seats. I request a group prayer and ask him to include the whole "cheek" part again as I found it particularly comforting the first time. He smiles, remembering, and nods. We all hold hands while he prays.
Suzanne Link

When I got home that evening, I told my wife about the exam but nothing about my going into shock over such a minor procedure. My weekend was anything but normal. I spent time in front of the TV, but not watching or listening. I began to wonder if I might really have cancer. My thoughts wound around and around in my head, and for quite a while I prayed. I think that this was the first time in my life that I prayed with the connecting idea of mortality as part of my prayer. I was 50 years old.
Dave Bartemes

The spiritual side of the journey taught me to just be happy where I am, instead of always thinking that I have to do more or be more. I don't have to make such high demands of myself. Maybe that's why I got sick. I was constantly thinking I should try harder. The truth is, at this moment in your life, you are right where you're supposed to be. That's the lesson.
Kelly Schall as told to Steven Peralta

There is a sense of calm, tempered by faith. There is a generosity that prevails. Enough just might be everything. I know this now.
Kelly Lamb

Kathmandu

A $2,000 Day

Doesn't everything die at last, and too soon?
Tell me, what is it you plan to do with your one
wild and precious life?

Mary Oliver

Kilimanjaro

If we lived forever, wasting a day of our life would be trivial. But we don't live forever. That's what makes today so valuable. If we're lucky, we will live to the average life expectancy in the U.S. of 78. If we're very lucky, we may live to be a hundred. Even so, millions of years passed before we were born, and millions more will pass after we're gone. For most of human history, the world will have been without us. Our imperative is to find meaning and joy in the little dash of time we're given between birth and death.

In every conversation I have with a cancer patient, whether we acknowledge it or not, the fact of death is present in the room. Mortality can be a powerful teacher.

Memento mori. So goes the Latin phrase "Remember, you must die." Daily reflection on the knowledge of our mortality can remind us to live today and every day with a greater sense of awareness and joy. It is not an invitation to sulk or mourn. It is a trumpet blast to wake you up to the possibilities that today presents to you.

Some of us are by nature procrastinators. We will put off doing things that we know we should do for as long as we can get away with it. I will confess, if my editor didn't give me a deadline, I'd never get anything written. The most powerful deadline of all is the search for meaning and purpose in a body that is dying by the second and will one day be gone.

I think most people who have never been

in a cancer center would be amazed by the joy and happiness contained within the walls. Life intensifies with a diagnosis of cancer. *Memento mori* is not just an abstraction. It is real and present. You'd think people living with cancer would want to take it easy, but I can tell you, some choose to climb mountains instead. Encouraged by their brush with death, they choose to actively engage with today, no matter how many more—or few— days they have left.

The Roman Stoic Seneca wrote: "Let us prepare our minds as if we come to the very end of life. Let us postpone nothing. Let us balance life's books each day."

My rough translation: We should all choose to live like we were dying.

Kathmandu

This hour is never coming back. Everything is passing so quickly. Only yesterday, I was your age! It doesn't matter how old you are, there's no guarantee of tomorrow. I think about this all the time: you can leave your house or this restaurant, enter the street and get hit by a car. But we never think of that possibility, so it doesn't frighten us. And yet we are scared of cancer. We are scared of heart attacks. Anything can happen.
Sanja Agic-Hajric

The truth is, I have never thought of myself as a particularly courageous person. Yes, I survived breast cancer, chemotherapy and radiation. But that was survival, not courage. I actually felt an indescribable peace as I was going through treatment. I wasn't afraid of dying. I knew where I was going when I died, and I figured I would get to see Bobby, my younger brother, again. He was 30 years old when we lost him to a brain tumor, 18 years ago now. We were inseparable growing up, so I was kind of excited at the thought of seeing him again. Don't get me wrong: I don't want to leave this world anytime soon. I want my grandbabies and even great-grandbabies to know their Grammy. It's just that I know something better is waiting on the other side. So dying didn't scare me. But climbing Mount Kilimanjaro? That took courage.
Tammy Blaede

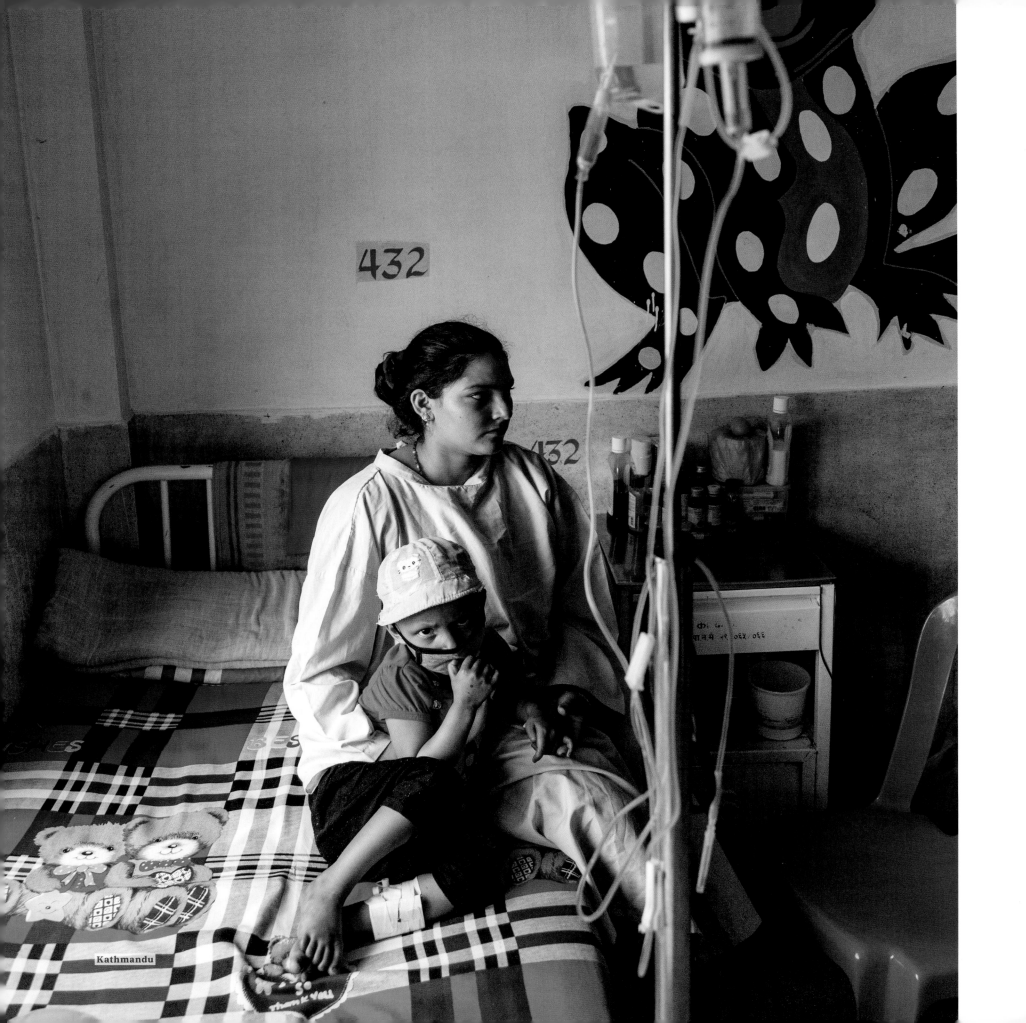

Our group moved on to the river in Kathmandu. Through the open bus windows it was easy to see spirals of gray smoke rising from the riverbanks. The acrid smell of burning flesh filled our nostrils with an odor that wouldn't leave for days. This was not the sparkling Colorado River where I had once enjoyed trout fishing. This was a river where people with no transportation traveled countless miles to cremate their loved ones in the short amount of time Buddhist tradition allows. It was such a public mourning. It felt invasive to watch. Was there solace or was it a celebration? It wasn't apparent to me from my side of the river, where carefree monkeys performed acrobatics from the trees. I watched as young children sifted through the wicker baskets of the hot ashy remains, looking for gold, silver or anything else that might be of value. How young these children were to experience something of such intensity. As we moved back to the parking lot, our group was surrounded by peddlers selling everything from jewelry to puppets. I couldn't help but feel a bit disrespectful buying trinkets when there was a young woman across the river saying goodbye to the love of her life.

Kelly Lamb

Dylan Little

The doctor came in and sat down on the edge of the ultrasound table, where I lay. "My guess is that it's cancer, and a fairly aggressive form of it. Your mammogram from last April was perfectly clear. Would you be able to wait an hour while we change the mammogram machine over to do a biopsy? We'll cancel our next appointment." In that moment the security of my warm October world was overshadowed by the uncertainty of what was ahead. Too numb for anything else, I agreed.

Connie Duinink

My thoughts were racing but I felt a strange focus. It's not like I thought I would die, but I did start thinking about who would come to my funeral. Who would actually be glad to pay their respects, and who would just be there out of social obligation, maybe even resenting the time and money it cost them to be there? Then I started thinking I should just walk out into the snow-covered fields, put one foot in front of the other for as long and far as I could walk until I dropped to the ground, feeling the kindness of the cold hard earth. Even now, it brings me a kind of peace to think about it. I could just start walking into the world and keep walking until I die.

Andy Fleming

Cancer has been a source of new insight, friends and opportunities that nurture and bring joy into my life. Yet at the same time, cancer puts my life in peril. Some might say it should be easy for me to understand that if I had not developed cancer, other good things would have come into my life without imperiling it. Cancer has become a spiritual teacher, assigning me this provocative, living kōan to solve sooner than expected. I learned something important in those brief periods of being present, experiencing the interconnection of my feet walking on mountain paths in Nepal. Peace was there.

Judith Allen

So what does it take to shake the carbonated bottle of passion and uncork it for every day, every moment you're blessed to own, with or without the urgency spurred from the reminder that all our days are numbered?

Tibet

Cancer, even when it is ultimately curable, reminds us that we are mortal. It reminds us what we already know—that we are going to die someday, even if it isn't because of cancer. It also reminds us that we are alive today, and that's a blessing. It's ironic, but cancer, which can kill you, can actually teach you how to live. It has the power to wake us up and inspire us to pursue lives of purpose, passion and compassion. In the end, death is not a failure or something to be feared; it's a motivator, a call to action, to live today to the fullest. The more we can be present in the moment, the more peace and joy we will experience in our life.

Michael Cuesta as told to Emilyn Crabbe

Ann was diagnosed in August, I think. We went through radiation with Dr. Deming and then chemo with the other oncologists, and we made it to March. The scans just kept improving, so the Browns, good friends of ours, planned to throw us a party to celebrate the positive stuff. This was great, except that the morning of the party we got the test results from a couple of days earlier. Ann's cancer was back. She was very clear about not wanting anyone to know. So here we are trying to celebrate, keeping the disappointing news at bay. We went through this lovely party with our friends, and it turns out that was the beginning of the end.

Kent Zimmerman

No one, not even the CEO of a major insurance company, receives an advance notification, a "heads-up" or fair warning before hearing those dreaded three words: "You have cancer." So what does it take to shake the carbonated bottle of passion and uncork it for every day, every moment you're blessed to own, with or without the urgency spurred from the reminder and realization that all our days are numbered?

Debra Peckumn

Tibet

Having cancer has heightened my awareness of what cancer patients go through, and I'm glad that I can share with them. So when somebody with cancer talks to me about it, I can now share and hope that my sharing can help them not be afraid. Because cancer doesn't mean "the D word." It doesn't mean death. It's about your attitude, about what's in your heart.
Miriam Tyson

Of course, we are all going to die, so it's just this idea that you're moving forward with life—you're doing your career, you're doing the family thing, and then *boom*. You have to face this thing. For me, I hope it's a healthy journey. I even try to be mindful—not in a bad way—about my own mortality. I'm a spiritual person, so I do ask some of the big questions, like what is life? I just don't want to get so busy with everything that I forgot to think about the big picture.
Cassity Gutierrez

There's a taboo in talking about cancer. Death is not the scary thing; it's a scary thing for the people who love you. The scary thing for the patient is the suffering and indignity. Often, other people don't want to hear this part. I know for a fact that a lot of people think talking about dying makes them more likely to die. For me, talking about dying was incredibly helpful and comforting.
Melisa Klimaszewski

Kathmandu

My daughter takes Japanese class at Central Academy, and I'm friends with the Japanese teacher, who said to me, "Audrey wants to go on this trip next year to Japan for spring break 2020." And the first words out of my mouth were "Do you need a chaperone?" That's when I realized that I never used to make plans very far in advance. I just wasn't able to think that far out. But now I'm telling myself, "I'm gonna go! I'm gonna go to Japan in March of 2020. I'm gonna be there. I'm going to go." It felt so good to think, "I can do that. I'm just gonna do that." I think it does weigh into every decision. You wonder if you're going to be able to commit something like that.
Kristi Meyer

As I type these words, I'm floating on zombie pills, not a care or a pain in the world for now—though I'm anxious for what the evening brings. Will I wake up in a pool of sweat, seriously disturbed by the events of a short oxycodone-induced dream again? Will Alicia have to wake up again worrying about me? Hoping we both sleep like babies tonight.
Justin Anderson

You know, a lot of times we plan something and it doesn't work out that way. When I was younger, I would say, "I'm gonna go somewhere" or "I'm gonna do something," and my mother always reminded me to say, "I plan." That's *my* plan. But then there's another plan, and it's God's plan.
Miriam Tyson

Going through cancer treatment is kind of like being able to go to your own funeral, but in a good way. Everyone you know comes out to tell you that they love you and why they love you. You learn what people see in you, what they appreciate about you, what your strengths in terms of relationships really are. Phone conversations often end with "I love you" instead of "goodbye."
Sue Mixdorf

Let's say there's an incurable cancer that can be treated with a pill that costs about $2,000 a day. That means about $600,000 a year for this drug. So if your best friend, your mother or father or you, yourself, got diagnosed with this cancer and they told you the cost, how would you feel? How long would you take the pill? What would you do to obtain it? Would you put your family in debt? Somebody has to pay, and it's not going to be the government. It's not going to be your insurance. It's not going to be your parents. I think about this all the time. I ask people: did you live a $2,000 day today? What's interesting about it is that $2,000 isn't $25,000. That's an amount that might make you decide to live three really good days of life and then call it quits. But $2,000 is the kind of money where you could imagine someone saying it'd be worth it to pay $100,000 for their child to live 50 more days. And then what about if you had to pay $10 to live every day? Would you live forever? (It's a good deal, take it.) $2,000 a day changes your perspective. At the end of the day, I sometimes think, would I have taken the pill today? Did I live a $2,000 day?
Michael Zimmerman

Death was never an option for me.
Michelle Flattery

Kathmandu

The Best Gift Ever

This is a wonderful day.
I've never seen this one before.

Maya Angelou

Nepal

I remember my very first trip to the Himalayan Mountains. I joined up with a major mountain-climbing expedition in Kathmandu to ascend one of the lesser-known peaks. Like a good former Boy Scout, I showed up well-prepared, toting my new coat, new hat, new backpack and new sleeping bag. To be on the safe side, I'd packed an extra hat, coat, and gloves. You get the picture. My backpack, crammed full of all this stuff, created a very heavy load.

Our week-long trek began in the Eastern Development Region of Nepal, up a river path that led to the technical climb of the snow-covered peaks. It didn't take long for me to realize that all the extra stuff on my back was not only unnecessary, it also was literally a burden. In the villages we traversed, I met plenty of people who could make better use of it. What did I need with all of this gear? I

quickly looked for opportunities to give away the burden I was carrying and make others happy in the process.

A cancer diagnosis is a different sort of burden, and it's never welcome news. But it has the ability to clarify the many blessings in our lives. Priorities shift. We can even learn to be thankful for the difficulties we encounter along our path, which can help—or sometimes force—us to find our inner strength, develop our creativity and learn how to innovate. Often, patients experience an outpouring of love, concern and assistance from family, friends and caregivers as they undergo cancer. From this, gratitude springs. We are reminded of our interconnectedness to one another and to the entire web of the universe.

I remember very clearly another trek in 2017 when our group of cancer survivors and caregivers descended the summit of Mount

Kilimanjaro. Never had I anticipated with such joy the prospect of a hot shower in that modest Tanzanian hotel that awaited us. At home, if I can hold on to even a fraction of that gratitude on a daily basis as I experience the little luxuries that modern life affords me, I will be forever changed.

An increasing body of scientific research links gratitude to improvement in patients' quality-of-life outcomes and psychological well-being. Grateful people report greater satisfaction with life and have lower levels of stress and depression. They are also more empathetic, kind and generous.

That's why I like to begin every day and every talk with this expression of gratitude:

It's a great day to be alive!

No matter what transpired yesterday or what tomorrow brings, we have today. And within the confines of today we have all that we need to find joy.

Tibet

I've received calls from all across the United States from people that I've known over the years as they find out about the fact that I am a cancer survivor and have experienced a different kind of journey in my life. I feel very thankful to have all these friends. I feel very thankful to know the people I know. And I feel very thankful to even begin to understand what this is all about. I'm not going to say that I totally understand all of it, but I'm not the guy that's going to sit there and say, "Why me?"

Frank Owens

I think we would all like to be like Dr. Deming, but some of us have to sleep at night. There is a miraculous quality about that man.

Mary Gottschalk

I have spent many hours musing on this fantastic experience; in fact, it gets more fantastic with each passing day. You see, a group of 41, most of us strangers, gathered together and over the course of two weeks became a family of 41. How fortunate to have gained so many great people in my life over such a short period of time. My new family members are back to their routines of work and family now. Some are even back to their "cancer routines." But this does not mean that they are forgotten. We have a special bond, we Kili-Trekkers, and I hold all of you dearly in my heart. I will be forever grateful and blessed for this unbelievable opportunity.

Sarah Selinger

Gena Haselhuhn

My experience on the mountain opened my eyes to recognize that God's promised right hand is often present in those He sends to come alongside us. I'm quite sure His hand sometimes looks like Mary or one of several others who carried my backpack when I could not. I'm just as sure that right hand looks like Jim, who had surveyed our weary group of trekkers and decided I was the person who most needed some extra help that day. Certainly His hand had directed Sarah to stand in the cold at Mass that night so she would be there to offer a strong arm as I staggered back to the tent. And one evening, a hand that looked a lot like Dr. Deming's came carrying a bowl of rice and curry sauce at dinner when my energy was fading and miles of hiking still lay ahead. God's hand restored my strength through the many generous hands of others—Teresa, Annie, Jena, Sheryl and many more.
Connie Duinink

I look at people who don't have kids, or young women who haven't started a family yet, and I realize there is something wonderful about being a mom and going through this. When I was lying in bed on the weekends, trying to recover from the chemo, it was awesome to hear their giggling, just to hear their energy, their life. Of course it was scary. I'd think, *Is this going to be my life now? Me lying here while they're outside?* More than anything, though, it energized me to hear them play. Sure, it was a distraction. But what a wonderful distraction.
Cassity Gutierrez

It is not because both of my breasts were surgically removed, or because of the poisonous chemotherapy and burning radiation I endured. It's not because I lost my hair and was bald for nine months of my life. And it's certainly not because I went from being in good shape to being 40 pounds heavier thanks to steroids and inactivity while sick. I am thankful for all that breast cancer taught me. And the most important lesson was this: I am loved.
Sue Mixdorf

I felt like I was going to burst into tears and jump up and hug Dr. R's assistant. We don't know for sure if it's the Eflornithine, the Lomustine, God, goat sacrifices, the prayers, the camping trips with Alicia and our dog Kujo, the hugs from the ones I love or the low-carb diet I haven't been following. But it's all working. The tumor is shrinking substantially, and we're one step closer to getting through this journey.
Justin Anderson

I would pull the cord to call the nurse, and within a minute someone was there. The care I got there was second to none. I don't know if anybody else could've given me better care. And I remember asking my girlfriend at one point to go check and see if there were any other patients in the hospital, because the care was that good!
Miriam Tyson

I had what is known as a "nurse navigator" who showed up to every single appointment—testing, results, you name it—and basically checked in with me after the doctors left the room. Donna was her name. She was just an angel, and that's not an overstatement. The doctors would leave and she would say, "Okay, how do we feel about this?" Later, when I first found out I was cancer-free, I lay on her floor with my feet on her desk. I thought I was gonna pass out. She just sat with me while I waited for them to finalize the results saying I was clean.
Michael Zimmerman

I was scared every day that I wouldn't make it. That I couldn't make it. I hated being sick and cold and unable to breathe. I hated the inconvenience of no electricity, hot water or flushable toilets. I hated wearing dirty clothes every day. But you know what? I would do it all again in a heartbeat. It was without a doubt the single most life-defining trip I could have ever taken. The best gift ever.
Karen Parman

I took care of everything and everybody and I thought I had my shit together. I didn't need help from anyone. Had I cooked dinners and given rides and shoulders to cry on when my friends were going through hard times? Yes. But could I accept help when it was my turn? Not very easily. "People want to help," a friend counseled me. "Tell them how. It will make you feel better and it will make them feel better, like they are doing something in a situation where people don't know what to do." So I was showered with meals and rides for my kids, hats and scarves and lunch dates and coffee. I was so grateful to be surrounded by people who cared. I stayed home from work, slowed down and spent more time with my children and my family. The gift of a second chance gave me the focus and courage to face one of my worst fears. I looked it in the eye, endured and got stronger.
Dr. Leah Ecklund

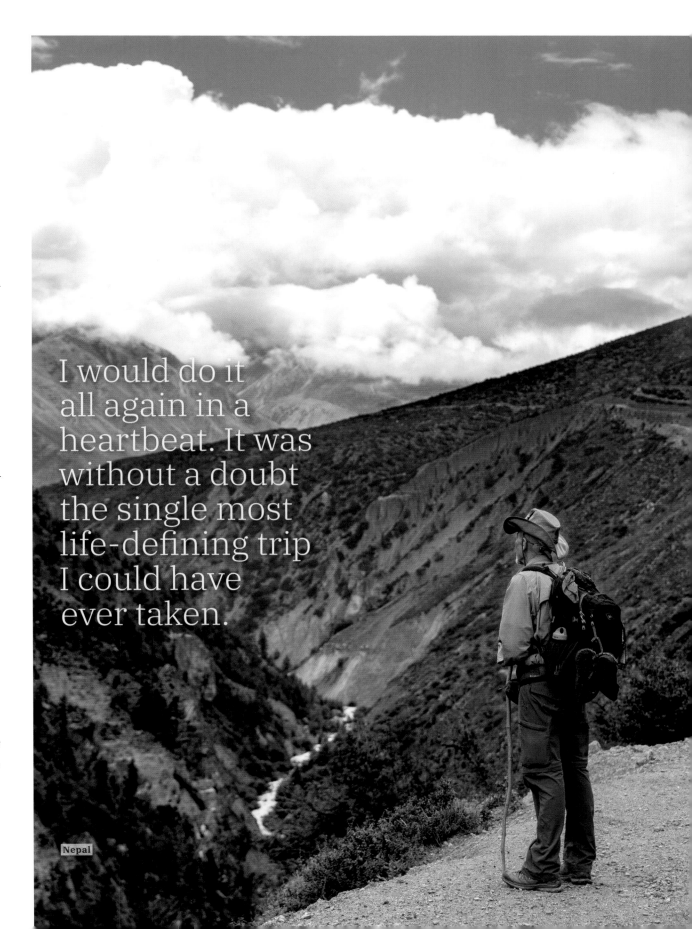

I would do it all again in a heartbeat. It was without a doubt the single most life-defining trip I could have ever taken.

Nepal

Tibet

I'm someone who has very few close friends outside of work. My career in law enforcement has cultivated a general distrust and often dislike of people in general. But the trek showed me a world that I didn't realize existed. The beauty and simplicity of the people of Nepal humbled and inspired me. It showed me how much good there really is in the world.
Trace Kendig

Suffice it to say that breaking bread together, sharing blessings, encouragement and laughter, relishing quiet moments of understanding, and bonding with new friends all made for a deeper connection for each of us as we gathered together around the table.
Dianne Jones

In 2010 when I was fighting brain cancer, I took a chemotherapy drug called Temodar, a very targeted medication that attacks brain cancer with minimal side effects to the rest of the body. Other than a little fatigue, I don't remember having many side effects from the drug, which is pretty incredible. My oncologist stayed until all of our questions got answers. He left us all with the feeling of hope, something I soon learned he's very good at. In his line of business, you need to be good at this. It's one of the reasons why I've started calling him "the coolest man in the world I wish I'd never met."
Jeff Lawrence

Last October I passed the three-year anniversary of my breast cancer diagnosis. I am very thankful for a dedicated and knowledgeable team of doctors who mapped out my treatment. I am deeply grateful for three years of restored health. I believe it is time for me to move beyond my personal restoration and find ways, as Dr. Richard Deming often put it, to reduce the burden of cancer in my community. The huge challenge of climbing a mountain like Mount Kilimanjaro is already providing me with invitations to speak to area groups about that experience. I am looking forward to raising hope and awareness about meeting the challenges of cancer.
Connie Duinink

This was chemotherapy after all. It is my understanding that Temodar is now the standard first line treatment along with surgery and radiation for brain cancer. The brave cancer fighters who signed up for a clinical trial years before were the ones who made Temodar possible for people like me. I am grateful for those people, and I am grateful that now with my participation in my own clinical trial, I may have the opportunity to help others diagnosed with brain cancer.
Justin Anderson

"Hello?" I ask, wondering if anyone can hear me an ocean away. "Mommy, Mommy... is that you?" The sound of my daughter's voice sends goose bumps up my arms. "Guess what, Mommy? I made my first two baskets today!" She can't see my smile, but I think she feels it. "Congratulations, sweetie," I tell her. "Your hard work and persistence have paid off." Because I'm a mom, I have to add, "Your role on the team is more than making baskets, you know." Then a wave of guilt rinses away my joy. I wasn't there for her. How could I have missed that moment? But I have to console my conscience. Moms give, but not just on the home front. From the other side of the world, my sweet, curious girl explodes with questions. "Mommy, where are you... what is Africa like... are you okay?" Her questions make my heart sing.
Mary Van Heukelom

We are so fortunate to have these doctors in Iowa. My husband and I went to see one doctor after I received my biopsy, and she was just amazing. She went from A to Z. And when she got to Z, she asked, "Any questions?" None. She was so thorough.
Miriam Tyson

Kathmandu

Dear Heavenly Father, Thank you for bringing us safely to the beginning of a new day, a day where, once again, we celebrate the gift of life. We thank you for bringing this group together, for our teamwork, and for the ongoing opportunity to learn about one another and to build new friendships. The camaraderie we have created is powerful. Please place your healing hand on those among us who are struggling physically or emotionally or who simply need a little energy. We thank you so much for our kind and helpful Sherpa friends as they guide our every step up the mountain with watchful eyes to keep us safe. Bless this food they have prepared. May it sustain us on our challenging journey this day. We offer you thanks and praise as we undergo this day.

Help us enjoy the beauty and every blessing that it holds. We ask these things in your name. Amen.
Linda Hoskins

Trace and I were tentmates in 2011 when we went to base camp at Mount Everest. He is a no B.S., tough-as-nails kind of guy. He's got bigger muscles and more guns than anyone I know. He's not afraid to tell me to suck it up and stop being such a wuss from time to time as he sees fit, even though I have brain cancer. It's what I love most about Trace. He wastes no time at dinner lecturing me about my pain pills in his own Trace way.
Justin Anderson

Nepal, Photo by John Richard

Of course, being a survivor is not just what the cancer has taken from us but what it has given us as well. It has given us freedom to care a lot less about what strangers might think of us as we yank off our wigs in public during brutal hot flashes. It has given us strengthened relationships with our spouses and families as we cocoon with those we love most during our vulnerable days. It has shown us how many neighbors, friends and co-workers care about us as the help, the food and the emotional support arrive at the doorstep. It has helped us put our problems in perspective and not take our blessings for granted. It has given us an opportunity to see how important it is to give and receive empathy and compassion. It has shown us how resilient we are and how good it feels to be an inspiration to others and ourselves. Facing our cancer has given us the courage to climb a mountain.

Leah Dietrich

I was exhausted the last two hours of the climb. The only thing that kept me going was my son, Jed, who got behind me, put his hands on my hips and pushed me forward, saying, "Step, Dad. Step, Dad. Step." You can't imagine what this did for me. It gave me the strength to keep pushing upward. Then there was Brandon, who said that I was an inspiration to him. I remember thinking to myself, *How can I be an inspiration to anyone when I can hardly put one foot in front of the other?* Then there was Dr. Deming. What can I say about this man? He kept telling me, "You can do it with two new knees and a new hip. You *rock*." He told me that without all the encouragement, I could very well still be sitting on that mountain, unable to go on. All the love, all the caring, all of the hugs, the working as one—these are the things that made it all a glorious climb. I climbed Mount Kili. I get to say that. But even better, I made the most wonderful and loving friends a person could ask for.

Steve Reblensky

There is nothing like meeting your new husband's ex-wife for the first time when you have very little hair, eyebrows or eyelashes to make you get over yourself. I also think that trauma bonding strengthened my young marriage. My husband and I were wed on a Saturday, and I started treatment the following Wednesday. When my tresses started to appear on my pillow and swirl down the drain, I asked him to shave my head. As in the beautiful Leonard Cohen song, "Hallelujah," he put me in a kitchen chair and cut my hair—that is, after pouring me a huge Scotch, lighting a candle and starting Coltrane on the stereo. After my mane was buzzed off, I looked into his eyes and saw nothing but love.

Rebecca Christian Patience

Before her team took off from the camp, Dee distributed her precious belongings to others. I got a big roll of toilet paper, something I needed pretty desperately. You know, some folks are always thinking of others.

Tomoko Yajima

Once we got back into bed and began our usual pre-sleep routines of staring at our iPhones and watching old episodes of "Friends," Alicia turned to me and made it a point to chat about things that she knew would keep my mind off my fear. She made me put my phone down so I wouldn't stay up all night waiting for the symptoms Google warned me were about to kick in. She was far more prepared for this night than I was. Sometimes I make fun of her for being so organized, but it's during moments like these that I really appreciate her structured ways.
Justin Anderson

Soon enough, I pulled myself together and Charlie took a great picture of me with Kim and our Sherpa. I look horrible, but it's one of my favorite pictures of the trip. Strangely, I am appreciative of the fresh wave of despair that overtook me. As time goes on after losing a loved one, the intense emotion fades and we have to pick up and carry on. However, I don't want to forget how precious Debbie, Terry, Grandma and Sherry are to me, nor how awful it is that they were stolen from this world too soon. On that mountain, at that moment, I was honoring them with my tears and anguish, thanking them for helping me make my way.
Mary LaPrairie

From Justin bitching about his catheter and not being able to pee (while peeing), having his nurses tell him he is their favorite patient by far today, telling all of us he loves us repeatedly, speaking English (as opposed to Mandarin) and having great movement in all his limbs, today was a success. Whatever mountain he has to climb tomorrow will come, and he will kick that one's ass, too.
Alicia Anderson

Kenya

The Hug I Need

If you want others to be happy, practice compassion.
If you want to be happy, practice compassion.

Dalai Lama

Nepal, Photo by John Richard

My friend Monsignor Frank said to me, "You know, Doc, it's too bad you don't speak Latin."

It was 2012, during our trek up to Mount Kilimanjaro. Out there on the trail, I had been trying to articulate to him something I had witnessed many times in my practice but couldn't quite explain: the relationship I sensed between suffering and compassion.

"Why Latin?" I asked.

"Because if you knew Latin, the connection would make perfect sense," said Monsignor Frank. "In Latin, the word for suffering is passion. Think of The Passion of Christ."

Here was my epiphany on the side of an African mountain, brought to me by this 79-year-old Catholic priest, who was also a survivor of prostate cancer. Compassion comes from the ecclesiastical Latin *compati*, meaning *to suffer with*. It is our own suffering that allows us to recognize the suffering experienced by others.

In 2013, Christina, a 37-year-old breast cancer survivor, was diagnosed with stage II breast cancer in her right breast. She went through successful surgery, chemotherapy and subsequent radiation therapy, only to develop cancer in her left breast two years later. Further surgery, chemotherapy and radiation therapy ensued, and Christina's treatment was, again, a success. In 2017, she journeyed with Above + Beyond Cancer to Nairobi, Kenya, to help cancer patients in Kenyatta National Hospital. Then she climbed with us to the summit of Kilimanjaro. Profoundly grateful for all those in her life who have supported her on her journey through cancer, Christina now wants to pay it forward. Since returning home, she has developed a nonprofit charitable organization to help cancer patients who are struggling with the financial burden of out-of-pocket expenses as they navigate our fractured health care system.

Christina transformed her own suffering into compassion for others. That is, she didn't just empathize with fellow cancer patients on the other side of the world; she also reached out to help relieve their suffering. Time and time again I have seen cancer survivors transform their own lives into ministries of compassion and generosity for others. Compassion is not just a feeling; it involves action.

"If we see a person who is being crushed by a rock," the Dalai Lama tells us in *The Book of Joy*, "the goal is not to get under the rock and feel what they are feeling; it is to help to remove the rock."

Like a hug, compassion is reciprocal. I get what I give. And there is no limit to the world's supply of compassion. It isn't going to run out. In fact, it is self-generating. In my practice as a physician, it became clear to me that treating patients with compassion—true and deeply felt compassion that springs from the desire to provide healing—has the capacity to improve a patient's quality of life.

Not all patients can be cured, but all patients can be healed.

Patients often tell me, "I feel so much better after I meet with you." But I'm not special. That is compassion at work, the driving force behind all that I do. What started off for me as a career in medicine has become a ministry of healing. I have found that a doctor-patient relationship founded in compassion is tremendously healing not just for the patient, but for the physician, too.

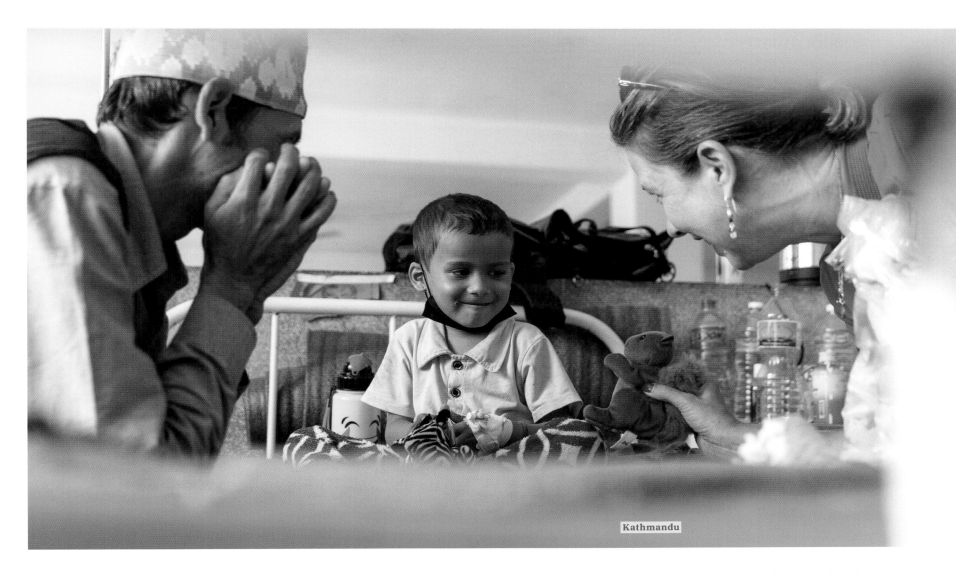

Kathmandu

Cory had a fear of heights, so when we faced the steep, rocky paths one morning, Scott rose to the occasion. A triathlete, Scott spends most of his time back home coaching swimmers who have a fear of water. He knew how to support Cory and how to get him to conquer the sheer rock walls. Scott's wife, Gail, was there at day's end to comfort him. I watched her embrace the shaken and exhausted young man. The word *peace* came to mind then. Gail was like a quiet shadow watching over Cory, an invisible but powerful spirit there to protect him.
Tomoko Yajima

I told one of the deacons from my church, "If anybody wants to talk about cancer, they can call me." That's not something I would have done two or three months before I got my diagnosis, because I'm just a private person. "You just don't talk." That's what my classmates and colleagues would have said about me before. But now, I can share with people going through this. Now I can understand. Now I can help somebody else.
Miriam Tyson

I see the fear in his eyes as he struggles to know how to help me. He is trying so hard to be positive, to be my rock. He *is* my rock.

Kilimanjaro

Kathmandu

For a small-town girl, this was the big city. I had many relationships with coworkers, friends and neighbors, but these people never seemed to care much about me. Then they showed up. They brought me food and cared for my toddler and took her to the park so I could rest. People really are generally good, I realized. They can surprise you, even when things aren't so great. That was a real lesson for me.
Kristi Meyer

Feeling ashamed and childish, I broke down, sobbing to the group that I couldn't go any farther. I was so exhausted I couldn't even think of where to place my foot next. "Just pass me!" I begged everyone. "Just go ahead." As I stood there, shivering and crying, one of our guides, Carlos, told me to give him my backpack. He already had his own pack, of course, so he hoisted mine on his front and took my hand. "Now, wedge your foot right here next to mine," he said. "Firmly." Step by step, Carlos guided me down the mountain.

He paused after every step to allow me to brace my foot against his. It went this way for hours. I honestly don't know how Carlos had the patience to lead me this way for so many miles. I knew I was slowing everyone down. But I have never in my life experienced such crippling fear. Then Dianne, one of my teammates, said to me, "We're in this together. We won't leave you."
Amy Colton

Kilimanjaro

I'm watching for symptoms, catering water. We slide over scree for two hours. It is tedious, a constant slip over steep, loose rock and dirt. Water supplies have melted and are dangerously low. I am down to one bottle. Bling Bling has none and needs something. She has been sick for days. I think of a plane crashing. Always put the oxygen mask on yourself first before assisting others. I envision a boat sinking and the captain swallowed by waters. I am angry with myself. This is not a burning plane, or the Titanic. We are not sinking into cold and murky waters. We are descending to our last camp. I unscrew my dusty cap and give my bottle to Bling Bling. I am a caregiver. She is a fighter. She is the inspiration. This team is my inspiration. This is my summit.

Mary Van Heukelom

My mother felt out of control over her body and her health. She was scared, and she needed someone to understand this. She needed someone to be the rational one, so she wouldn't have to. I was there to rein her in when she needed it, and to push her when she needed pushing. Sometimes she just needed to allow herself to be sick and dependent on others. It never really seemed that hard to me. I had to recognize, well, she's sick, and I've got to do this. I've got to make sure she's okay.

Michael Cuesta as told to Emilyn Crabbe

How would it feel, I wondered, to impact so many lives with so much caring and compassion? As if reading my mind, Dr. Deming turned to me with a partial smile and simply said, "Bittersweet."

Kelly Lamb

Maybe the little things we can do for others are the most important. Maybe I didn't need to go on a trip to make some heroic effort to help others—I could do it every day at home, at work, in my community.

Dr. Leah Ecklund

As I sat perched on my windowsill, a reflection in the window caught my eye. I found a stranger looking back at me through red-rounded, sunken eyes. Her pale lips, smooth bald head and tear-tracked face met my pitiful stare. I closed my eyes and took a deep breath. "How did I get to be like this?" I asked the stranger that looked back at me. I hugged my knees to my chest and rested my head on them, daydreaming back to happier times—school events, Friday nights and boyfriends. But like a fading echo, they felt dim and out of reach. The satisfaction and joy of those memories had lost their savor. "Those days aren't coming back," I told the stranger who looked back at me. I couldn't deny it any longer: this wasn't just a bad dream that would vanish with the dawn. *Yes, cancer is greedy,* the stranger told me. *It loves to take things from you.* But she told me it wouldn't take me, and it couldn't take my hope. I didn't ask the stranger to leave; I embraced her. *Your cancer journey isn't something you put in a box and stuff with the dust bunnies under your bed,* she said. *Use it as a tool.* The stranger gave me a permanent pair of magic sunglasses. *From now on, cancer and chemo aren't monsters*, she said. And cancer wouldn't be a death sentence. Instead, it would serve as the key to unlocking the woman I was meant to be. Everything looked rosier with my new frames on. I learned to see things as they really were. I learned to see what mattered: family, compassion, courage and gratitude. Life became beautiful when I directed my energy away from negativity and toward dreaming of the fullness life could bring me despite cancer.

Kristin Sumbot

From the very start, my husband is the shoulder I lean on, the hug I need and my companion through it all. I see the fear in his eyes as he struggles to know how to help me. He is trying so hard to be positive, to be my rock. He *is* my rock.
Joni Livermore

I'm a very impatient person, and I can be competitive. On my first journey with Above + Beyond Cancer, I was one of the people who stayed at the front of the pack. I wasn't trying to be first; it's just natural for me to move through everything quickly. But during this last trip, my goal was to slow down. I made a point of staying as far behind as I could, most of all at the beginning of the trip when the trek was especially rigorous. It helped me get to know my fellow trekkers more deeply. When you're always moving fast, you end up with the others who are doing the same. You miss the chance to know people who might be struggling or who are very intentionally moving at a pace that allows them to take in the landscape. A slower pace allows for meaningful conversation. It sounds so silly, but this pointed effort to slow down made a huge difference for me. I reminded myself that the reason I was there was to help people who needed a little extra help and to learn as much as possible about them, to hear their stories.
Yasmina Madden as told to
Allison Kaefring

I remember calling a coworker to tell him my news, that I had cancer. He started sobbing. And I remember thinking, *Screw you, man. Can't you hold it together until we get off the phone?* It made me resolve not to tell anyone anymore. And I didn't. I never put it on social media. I've never gone public with my story.
Michael Zimmerman

Mary Van Heukelom

No essay on the many faces of Nepal is complete without mention of the Sherpas, porters and cooks who accompanied us on our journey. Three weeks in their company put an end to my previous idea of Sherpas as little people dressed in fur, running up and down the mountains with their yaks. This image couldn't be further from the truth. They are educated, somewhat Westernized, industrious people. They know when the look on the face of a trekker signals trouble and are eager to step in. They know as much about the human spirit as they do about the ways of the mountains.

Like the rest of us, they want what is best for their families. There was tenderness for those who struggled and a word of encouragement for those whose courage wavered. A "what's mine is yours" attitude flourished in the villages, a welcome contrast to the dog-eat-dog, materialistic American culture of instant gratification. There were never complaints or harsh words. It made me realize: Westerners might appear to be climbing to the top, but are they really? My lesson from the Sherpas is that I can live a life of compassion without expectation, and that faith can get a person to the top.
Kelly Lamb

And I Shall Be Richer All My Life for This Sorrow

You will heal and you will rebuild yourself around the loss you have suffered. You will be whole again, but you will never be the same. Nor should you be the same, nor would you want to.

Elisabeth Kübler-Ross and David Kessler

Kilimanjaro, Photo by John Richard

Even if someday we could discover a cure for every cancer in the world, we would still need to learn how to grieve. Just as every one of us will experience death, before that, we will each have the opportunity to experience grief.

In her seminal work, *On Death and Dying,* Elisabeth Kübler-Ross described the process of dying as a passage in five stages: denial, anger, depression, bargaining and acceptance. These were later adapted by Kübler-Ross and David Kessler to describe the process of grieving as well. Kessler has since written about a sixth stage of grief: finding meaning.

As a human being and as a cancer physician, I have experienced grief, but it has taken many years for me to understand grief's meaning in my life. When I was a junior in high school, my mom was diagnosed with stage IV lung cancer. She died at the age of 52, while I was in medical school. I was not prepared to submit to

that grief. Then, just as I graduated from medical school, my dad, also age 52, died of sudden cardiac arrest. I was in the midst of my internship and decided that I didn't have time to experience that loss fully. Instead, I plowed through my work and studies. Now, after 35 years of practice, I have learned about grief and grieving from my cancer patients and their families. And I have grieved the loss of many patients I have come to know and admire in those years.

In March of 2016, my friend Charlie Cutler died of lymphoma at the age of 26. Charlie and I first met as patient and doctor on the day after Christmas in 2012 and came to forge a relationship of caring and trust until the time of his death. Charlie's long and winding cancer journey took him through the hallways of many medical centers in Iowa, Nebraska and Minnesota. He experienced chemotherapy and radiation treatments, cancer recurrences, two stem cell transplants and months of

hospitalization. Through it all, he continued to run, cycle, climb, work, laugh and dance. His intelligence and natural curiosity garnered him an "on-the-job" medical education that rivaled most medical students. He taught each of us, whether family, friend or caregiver, to live our lives with courage and gusto.

Although my grief was nothing compared to that of his parents, Charlie's death moved me to tears. He brought out the best in everyone he touched with his compassionate, introspective and joyful outlook on life. Although I'm wise enough to know that Charlie's death was not my fault, as one of his physicians I feel in some way responsible for our collective inability to save his life. That too was part of my grief.

As deeply as Charlie's friends and family felt his loss, the love and joy we derived from his short time on this planet was worth every ounce of grief.

We grieve because we have loved.

Nepal, Photo by John Richard

My sister would've thought my trip to Peru was the craziest thing. Peru was amazing, challenging and fulfilling in so many ways. A group of relative strangers journeyed across the world, then traveled on foot to an incredible, spiritual place. It came as no surprise that many of those strangers knew Lori; she was such a force in the Des Moines culinary world. She had trained some of the finest chefs in town and was always taking a souffle or a taco salad to a church event or neighborhood meeting. "What would Lori do?" was a common refrain when cooks got into difficult culinary situations. No surprise, then, that even in Peru, her presence echoed all around me. We had always talked about going on a trip together, but we never made it happen. Maybe next year, we always said. Then next year never came.

Kelly Donato

In the back of my mind was this question: what is the legacy of Anne and me? I toured the hospice facilities over at Kavanagh House probably two weeks before Anne died. "Gee, this is great," I said. I had never been into the idea of hospice; I really didn't want her dying in an unfamiliar place. I realized too late that the greatest gift I could have given her would have been hospice care at Kavanagh House where somebody else would take care of all her medical needs and keep her comfortable, leaving me to concentrate on just loving her. Contrast that with having to give her a morphine shot every two hours. Why didn't someone tell me? Or, more accurately, why wasn't I a smart enough caregiver to recognize these options?

Kent Zimmerman

I was 12 years old when Debbie, a friend of my family, died of breast cancer. She was 29, and I idolized her. As the disease ravaged her body, I tried to make deals with God. *Take my eyesight so she can be okay,* I prayed. *Take my ability to walk so she can be cancer-free.* The morning my dad came to wake me, he didn't have to say anything. Debbie, age 29, mom of two little boys, was gone. We put her body into the ground on a damp and dreary day. I had no idea what to do with the heartbreak that followed. I cried endlessly, couldn't eat and ignored friends' invitations. If I found myself laughing or enjoying even a moment, I lashed myself with feelings of extreme guilt.
Mary LaPrairie

When I did my first round of chemotherapy, my sister-in-law was pregnant with her second child, and she invited me to accompany her to her ultrasound. We all knew that due to my chemo, there was a good chance I would never experience my own baby's ultrasound. I watched as the doctor spread bluish gel on her bare belly. I held my breath as we waited for a heartbeat. At first, they couldn't find it, and my breath caught in my chest. Then it was there. The room exhaled. I shut my eyes, taking in the tiny, rhythmic whoosh of her heart. I heard my brother and sister-in-law breathing too. The room was pulsing, rhythmic. I smiled. The sound of that heartbeat, from a child who was not mine, rose in my ears. My chest tightened. Salty tears slipped into my mouth and dripped off my face, leaving dark, expanding circles on my shirt. I felt like I couldn't breathe. My chest felt cuffed. I needed air. I fled the doctor's office and left behind my sister-in-law with her unborn daughter. I escaped into the hallway and stood there, chest heaving and vision darkening. I reached for something to support me, but I still couldn't breathe. Until the sobs came.
Julie Goodale

Before my biopsy, I had actually joked with friends and family about not being the first reported case of "wrist cancer." I had never heard the word "sarcoma" before that diagnosis, but I certainly knew the word cancer. I was entering a narrow spot similar to one I had experienced when my sister, Kristin, died in 1991. A month before her 36th birthday, a recurrence of malignant melanoma metastasized into her lungs and brain. Kristin was the baby in our family, the sixth of seven children and seven years younger than I. She was also leaving behind a husband and two small boys. I spent nearly every Friday with Kristin during the last five months of her life. On one of those special Fridays, after spending some time sorting through her linen closet—Kristin wanted to leave an organized house, of course—we went to a movie, *The Fisher King,* with Robin Williams, and then out for Chinese food. In the midst of dinner, Kristin said she didn't even know why we were doing this. Eyes filled with tears, I answered, "Because we're creating memories."
Ruth Bachman

We arise with the sun and begin the task of stringing more than 800 prayer flags on strands of rope. Everything takes longer at this altitude, so I have to stop and catch my breath after every two or three steps. I stand and watch as others string flags. They hold them with such tenderness, and the flags seem to elicit sighs or tears. You can tell each one is a story. Then my brother Bobby's flag goes up next to Mom's and Aunt Mary's. The ropes are attached atop the glacier, three long strands curving in the wind, anchored to the ground. Green, red, yellow, blue and white flags flap wildly in the wind. This is the moment. It is why we are here. We remember, we honor and we are thankful.
Tammy Blaede

Holly Hansen

Many on the journey to Machu Picchu were celebrating the lives of loved ones who were battling cancer or who had lost their battle. We made prayer flags and had a ceremony during our journey. I walked along seeing hundreds of prayer flags made by so many individuals: mothers, fathers, sisters, brothers, friends, and the list goes on. My eyes rested on a flag I'd made at the last minute. My prayer flag had written on it: Paul and Michelle Flattery: Marriage August 5, 1994—Spring 2015. People spoke of their prayer flags and how they knew they would see their loved ones again. I stood up and said that I would never see my marriage again, because it had been destroyed forever. My Above + Beyond family showed their support with hugs, smiles and tears. We all have our cancers in life, not necessarily the illness itself.
Michelle Flattery

Kathmandu

I kept thinking that this was the hardest thing I've ever done. But it's not. Losing my friend Debbie was so much worse. I'm remembering the day she died as if it just happened, and I realize that was the worst pain of my life. Why is she gone? Why are so many people gone?

Mary LaPrairie

The day of our pedicure appointment, Wendy sent a text saying she needed to reschedule. Side effects from a recent chemo session were taking their toll. For some reason, I left the office and headed directly to my friend Tom, a florist. He'd know what an "upbeat, unique and memorable" bouquet would look like. "What's the occasion?" he asked, showing me fluffy chartreuse spheres, iridescent crimson crescents and ivory tear drops. "No real occasion," I said, "except that today is a day my friend might die." No

further explanation required. Floral selection complete. I grabbed a pen and a blank card and opened my heart. What would be meaningful to me if I knew I was living my final hours? I think I would want to know how I had impacted others—what and who my life had touched. So those were the words I wrote, words that ultimately became part of her printed obituary after she passed away just five days later.

Debra Peckumn

This last trip was the best time in my life. At one point, we were traversing the side of the mountains and you could see all the way up to the top of the glaciers. Then a vista opened: an enormous mountain loomed across an expanse where, below, a huge farming valley spread before us. For a split second I just stopped and looked around, and I could feel my family with me. I felt like I was sharing the moment with the people I had lost. It was a moment of elation, of happiness. My eyes welled with tears, just standing there in the gorgeous cold.
Michael Cuesta as told to Emilyn Crabbe

Floating in the wind are photos of friends who set out to scale peaks with us only a year or two ago, by whose side we had sat anxiously on airplanes, who allowed us to carry their baggage when they felt weak and who took on our load when they felt strong. The calm comfort of their presence remains with us in our minds and hearts even though we were separated too soon and without enough notice. Life hadn't asked for our consent.
Brian Triplett

One of the lessons I learned during the 26 months of John's illness and his subsequent passing was that our world and this life are full of trials, illness, death and experiences we do not understand. But there is a God who walks beside us always, even when we can't know or feel His presence. When John passed, I felt like my worldly life was over. John had gone to heaven to be with the Light of the world, and I entered the darkest period of my life, my Hell. That's what it felt like. All my joy, my light had disappeared. There were still times where I recognized God working in my life, but for a while I couldn't feel John, and I couldn't feel God's presence anymore. I thought I had lost them both.
Jo Kay Boyle as told as Abdullahi Salim

Tibet

I had threaded about 300 flags, so I can still feel it on my fingers. My goal on this journey was to focus on intangible ideas and the meaning of the relationships people created. So, for me, threading flags was a moment where I was able to physically connect with the experience of this journey. I was also struck by the emotional messages each flag represented. These flags were made by people across the nation, each of whom had a story. Some flags were sent in memory of a person who was lost, in celebration of another's survival or even as a reminder of the experience still to come. With each piece of fabric, there was "remembrance" or "honor" or "gratitude." Each flag represented not just an individual, but the relationships that individual had cultivated.
Seán Rose as told to Helen Trisko

The past two weeks I have been caring for my mother as her cancer takes over her body. We have spent hours talking about my experiences in Africa. She loved living it through my eyes, as if she was there herself. Cancer for me was hard, and the trek up Kili even harder. But caring for my mother was the toughest challenge yet. Kili prepared me for that challenge because it made me stronger, more compassionate, a better listener. Sadly, mom passed away yesterday. She is at peace now, and her pain is gone. My pain is the aching in my heart for the woman who loved me unconditionally.
Bev Lund

So as I hiked, carrying her flag, and then flying it, I prayed she would be one of the lucky ones, that she'd be a survivor. Regrettably, my prayer was not answered the way I had hoped. Now, she will never see the hundreds of daffodils that we planted around her house for her last fall, and I will be speaking at her memorial service this weekend.
Kathy Williams

Lori could be goofy, serious and playful. She loved to play on the fact that she was older than I was, and "Dad's favorite," or so she was told on occasion when they shared one-on-one time together. I was told the same thing, of course, when Dad and I had one-on-one time, and we both knew it. We would tease each other if we had to approach Dad about something difficult. "You ask him— you're his favorite," one or the other of us would say. Or "I'm the one who's got to do this, because I'm his favorite!" We'd share a sisterly laugh about it.
Kelly Donato

Natua's husband had lost his life after a terrible battle with prostate cancer. The disease had ravaged his body, she told me, before he had been properly diagnosed. Natua knew in her heart that it was cancer. I showed her the flags we carried with us, and I told her it would be an honor for me to carry a flag in her husband's name. As our flight made its descent to the Atlanta airport, she put the finishing touches on the red flag, tears gently streaming down her cheeks. She lovingly kissed the flag, and as she handed it to me, she shared a bit about her faith. I learned that she was from India and that her faith led her to believe that nothing happens by chance. She said she believed it was not a coincidence to be sitting across from me on our flight to Atlanta. This woman's brown eyes penetrated my soul as she kissed the red flag one last time and thanked me for helping to keep her husband's memory alive. Then we both brushed back tears and went our separate ways.
Diane Hammond

I remember navigating the new landscape of a freshly scarred body: the clothes that no longer fit, the muscles that no longer move the way we expect, the daily fear that this might be the day cancer comes back. But like just-picked flowers, the vividness of the color fades with the passage of time. Scars do fade. They never go away, but their vivid red diminishes. My own scars are grey, the color of weariness, the weariness I sometimes feel of a decade of survival. I cherish the beauty of the colors that fill my life, but of late I feel the pull of the losses.
Julie Goodale

I'm remembering the day she died as if it just happened, and I realize that was the worst pain of my life. Why is she gone? Why are so many people gone?

Kathmandu

Life Begins Again

Travelers, there is no path,
paths are made by walking.

Antonio Machado

Kenya

This is the lightly edited text of a letter I wrote to the Above + Beyond Cancer group that traveled to Kilimanjaro. It was emailed to the group on January 18, 2017, after our return home.

Dear Friends, I hope that all of you who flew back to the USA on Sunday made it home safe and sound.

First, I want to thank each of you for having the courage and confidence to join Above + Beyond Cancer on the journey to Africa. I know that the trip required a sacrifice in many ways—in your finances, your family responsibilities, and your careers. A trip like this requires a leap of faith. Thank you for your willingness to respond to the call. You may have thought you were just signing up for an adventure in Africa. I hope that you now realize you were embarking on a transformational journey—a pilgrimage—that has the power to change your life.

In some ways, the journey had a finite beginning and ending marked by transatlantic flights. But in other ways, the journey continues. I encourage each of you to take time to contemplate what happened during these past two weeks. We comprised a remarkable group, and our time together in Africa was powerful. Whether you hiked with us as a cancer survivor, a caregiver or as part of the staff, you took part in an incredible experience—a blessing, really. Contemplate this blessing. Learn from it; let whatever wisdom you may have derived from this pilgrimage illuminate your life and the lives of those around you.

You have brought many things from Africa back home with you. Yes, some of them are trinkets for family, friends or ourselves, but they are nothing in comparison to the self-knowledge you stand to gain as you reflect, write and share. In his book *The Art of Pilgrimage: The Seeker's Guide to Making Travel Sacred,* Phil Cousineau writes, "The story that we bring back from our journeys is the boon. It is the gift of grace that was passed to us in the heart of our journey. Perhaps it was in the form of an insight into our spiritual life, a glimpse of the wisdom traditions of a different culture, a shiver of compassion, an increment of knowledge. All these must now be passed on. The boon is a presence in the soul of the world that can be sensed and honored and carried home in your heart."

As you begin your life at home again, know that Above + Beyond Cancer will share photos and provide opportunities to celebrate our shared accomplishment together in person. I know that we will always have a connection with one another. Cherish those bonds. And don't ever stop learning and loving. Allow a sense of purpose and passion to thrive in your life.

One final aphorism borrowed from a beautiful song sung by Lee Ann Womack— "When you get the choice to sit it out or dance, I hope you dance."

With gratitude and compassion, your friend, Dick.

Nepal

I've heard other cancer patients in remission say they worry every day that their cancer will come back. I absolutely refuse to worry like that. If I can help even one person not think about cancer every single day, that would be great! Going into cancer treatment or getting a diagnosis can be terrifying, but maybe it gives you a different outlook on life that's better than the one you had before. We're afraid to make changes in our lives, and we put these restrictions on ourselves, but we should just go for it. We have nothing to lose, we never really do.
Kelly Schall

With this new understanding, we return home, blessed by the experience and filled with gratitude, forgiveness and compassion. We see our lives and all that fills our lives as the incredible gifts they are. Then, with this new sense of fulfillment and purpose, life begins again.
Charlie Wittmack

As my father and I step off the plane into the heat of Kathmandu, we are greeted with motorcycles and cars going every which way, people asking us where we're going, offering us rides. The welcoming team from Above + Beyond Cancer finds us, puts fresh flower leis around our necks, and we embrace in warm hugs. On this journey we put one foot in front of the other one million times as we hike towards Imja Tse. Every day I have a smile on my face through the happiness and the hardships of the journey. I no longer worry about how I will be remembered at my funeral. The journey to Nepal solidifies my understanding, one that began forming when I was diagnosed. What is most important to me is existing in the present moment and finding profound connections with the people and the world around me.
Andy Fleming

Kelly Schall

For five years, I carried this burden of guilt: I had failed to save Anne. I tried to make her comfortable to her last breath, and I don't think I succeeded. During my conversation with Mary and Brian in that Starbucks knock-off in Lukla, I realized that our failed trip up the mountain, Imja Tse, and the painful trip down unmasked a fear that had plagued me since my wife's death. The door to greater understanding had been opened, and when it was shared with two best friends, it let me understand and accept the failures of the past, freeing me to begin life again.
Kent Zimmerman

I have always wanted to help cancer patients, but it wasn't until I actually had cancer that I realized the different systems of support cancer patients might need. For one thing, we are not done healing when the treatments are done. We still deal with the aftereffects of the medications. We are still affected by cancer's emotional toll, not only on us, but on our loved ones as well. I want to use this trip and the things I realized about myself to help develop my voice as an advocate for people in treatment and in survivorship.
Michelle Flattery

Goals are not always black and white. Sometimes the effort and the execution are just as important as reaching the top or crossing the finish line. Pride in your accomplishment is still possible. I needed to give myself a break and enjoy the journey. After all, life is not about piling up the wins; it is a collection of experiences, good and bad. Those experiences make us who we are. We all went to Nepal for a transformational experience. I, like most, thought the transformation would occur from achieving the unachievable. Never did I imagine that it would come from not achieving the achievable.
Julie Hamilton

I'm starting to let go of some of my guilt. I'm sitting with it better than I used to. It might not ever go away, but I'm trying to feel better about it. The journey to Nepal and Tibet helped me realize that while I'll never achieve a complete sense of peace about the fact that Jen died while I survived, I have reconciled myself to my survivor's guilt.
Dana Downing

Why did you let me come here? Why am I doing this? And then this thought entered my mind: *I am doing this for them.* I am doing this for my children. What am I giving them by coming here? I am showing them that life can be better above and beyond cancer. I am showing them that things worth having are often difficult to obtain. I am showing them that God always turns bad into good if you let Him.
Cindy Torvik

Colorado

If cancer is the narrow spot in an hourglass and I am the sand, then I have traveled from the top through that tight spot to the bottom. When you go through that narrow spot, your sand is refined and redefined, sifting out interior resources not previously noticed or called upon. Life is full of narrow spots, not all labeled "cancer." However, cancer is the narrow spot that has given me the opportunity to look at life with a different perspective—not once, but twice. It informs the way I choose to live life every day.
Ruth Bachman

I think about something that's difficult. Right now, I have a million research papers to grade, for example. Or I worry about having to jog on the treadmill for three miles. But then I stop and think, "I had a brain tumor, so I'm pretty sure I got this. I can grade some papers, and I can run three miles. I can do anything." I can do it because I can.
Kristi Meyer

Yes, we are all survivors in some way. We are not the same people we were before cancer. Our families are not the same, either. Our bodies, our minds and our spirit are not the same as before cancer. But we can't go back to "before cancer." We have to go forward. We have to move beyond cancer. We have to climb above it. That's why we're here on this mountain, in this beautiful country, Nepal. We all want to move above and beyond cancer.
Leah Dietrich

Kilimanjaro, Photo by John Richard

I'd like to see someone put a stop to cancer, and I don't think it's too crazy to think that maybe it could even happen in my lifetime.
Justin Anderson

For many years while in my 20s and 30s I had a recurring dream: I am a participant in a spiritual community of men and women whose particular beliefs are not clear to me but who have learned to fly using the mind. Women in this community live in quarters separate from the men on different sides of a mountain. The men of the community have invited the women to join them for a spiritual ceremony and celebratory meal on their side of the mountain. In the next moment, the other women and I are flying higher and higher to go over the mountain and down to the other side to join the celebration. At this point in my dream I always begin falling. I am falling because I have lost mental focus or whatever form of awareness that was sustaining my flight. I panic, plummeting to the ground and trying to think harder, which doesn't work. I'm so frightened, falling faster and faster. But then I remind myself that thinking harder is not the key to flying. Correct mental focus and awareness are. Though still terrified, I redirect my mind to engage my awareness correctly. Sure enough, my falling slows, then ends. Slowly, I resume moving upward and forward. Then I wake up. Never do I get to the other side of the mountain! Every time I dreamed this story, I wondered what constituted correct mental focus and awareness, the kind that I understood in my dream but not when awake. What was it I was trying to teach myself over those many years?
Judith Allen

On this mountain, on Kilimanjaro, where life was stripped down to its most essential elements, no moment of crystalline clarity happened for me. I already knew that I was strong. I already knew that I would continue on. I already knew that unspeakable beauty and unbearable pain can exist in the same moment. On this climb, the truth played out for me in more subtle ways: the father, whose artificial joints weren't as strong as

his will, being helped up the mountain by his son; a pack being retrieved for a teammate as he stumbled into camp after dark, too tired to find it himself; a hand reaching out to steady me as I retched in the rocks; the eyes of someone whose thoughts were on her joy, half a world away.
Julie Goodale

Kathmandu

I could go around and around as many times as I wanted, but regardless of how many other paths I took, they would all lead me back to the beginning. "The only way out is through," I thought, and headed home.
Stefanie Stenberg as told to
Ren Culliney

Since returning from the trip, I feel a range of emotions. At first, I was angry—angry and sad that I hadn't reached out more to others. Then I felt jealous that everyone else seemed to walk away from the trip with great friendships and that maybe I hadn't. I even wrote a story about feeling like a ghost, like I was invisible. Now, months after returning, I have come to the realization that this was my role on the trip. It was my way of learning about myself and protecting myself so that I could be physically up to the challenge. Would I love to take the trip again, to have a do-over so I could build those friendships and be more "present" to others? Sure, but I can't. What I can do is to learn and grow from the trip that I did experience. The transformation is still taking place.
Sue Mixdorf

I don't believe people get cancer for a reason. There's no reason anyone has to get sick, injected with chemicals, blasted with radiation, undergo surgery, be saddled with huge medical bills and experience emotional trauma. But I do think we have to find reasons to live every day, to live with purpose and to provide others with opportunities to live a life with purpose. I'm someone who received a phone call that changed my life. It's one I wish I could have hit the ignore button on. I wish it had just been a wrong number. But it wasn't. The scary part is this: anyone could have received that phone call.
Andy Fleming

Now, as I wait for cancer to do what it's going to do, I see it all as this unbelievable trip, you know? I would be lying if I told you I never look back at pictures of myself during treatment or read my journal entries from that time without thinking, "I freaking *did* that." I lived that, and in some ways, I think it's really cool that I got the chance. I'm out of treatment now, and the further away I am from the epicenter of the cancer journey, the less real it feels. So sometimes I do like to be reminded that I lived that, that it happened.
Michael Zimmerman

Recently, I stumbled on this phrase attributed to Buddha: "You could search the whole world and never find anyone as deserving of your love as yourself." I now recognize that love really does live inside of me. If love can live in me, then I just gotta believe it must live in everyone else too, and those supposedly "really bad things" are part of the fiber that weaves all of us together.
Karla Hansen

Part of me longs to stay, to don bright colors and walk barefoot in red dirt. I long to flee the dung-colored hills of a snowless mid-winter back home. For now, though, I'll dress in shades of khaki and tan, and head farther west into the Serengeti in our tan jeep. Eventually, I'll return home, as planned. But I'll continue to dream in color, the colors of bee-eaters and sunbirds.
Julie Goodale

Sometimes, just like when we are running to catch the last train pulling out of the station, we try to keep hold of our loved ones and not let go. But the train departs, seemingly too early most times. Or perhaps right on time. We're angry because things like schedules, like life, are determined by tiny cells and mere seconds. But those things might just be going according to plan. Maybe we can't accept it, at least for a while. Maybe not until we meet again in another place down the tracks, in a town we can't correctly pronounce, in a land of unprecedented beauty, a place we can't altogether fathom until we get there.
Brian Triplett

Maybe we can't accept it, at least for a while. Maybe not until we meet again in another place down the tracks, in a town we can't correctly pronounce, in a land of unprecedented beauty, a place we can't altogether fathom until we get there.

Kansas

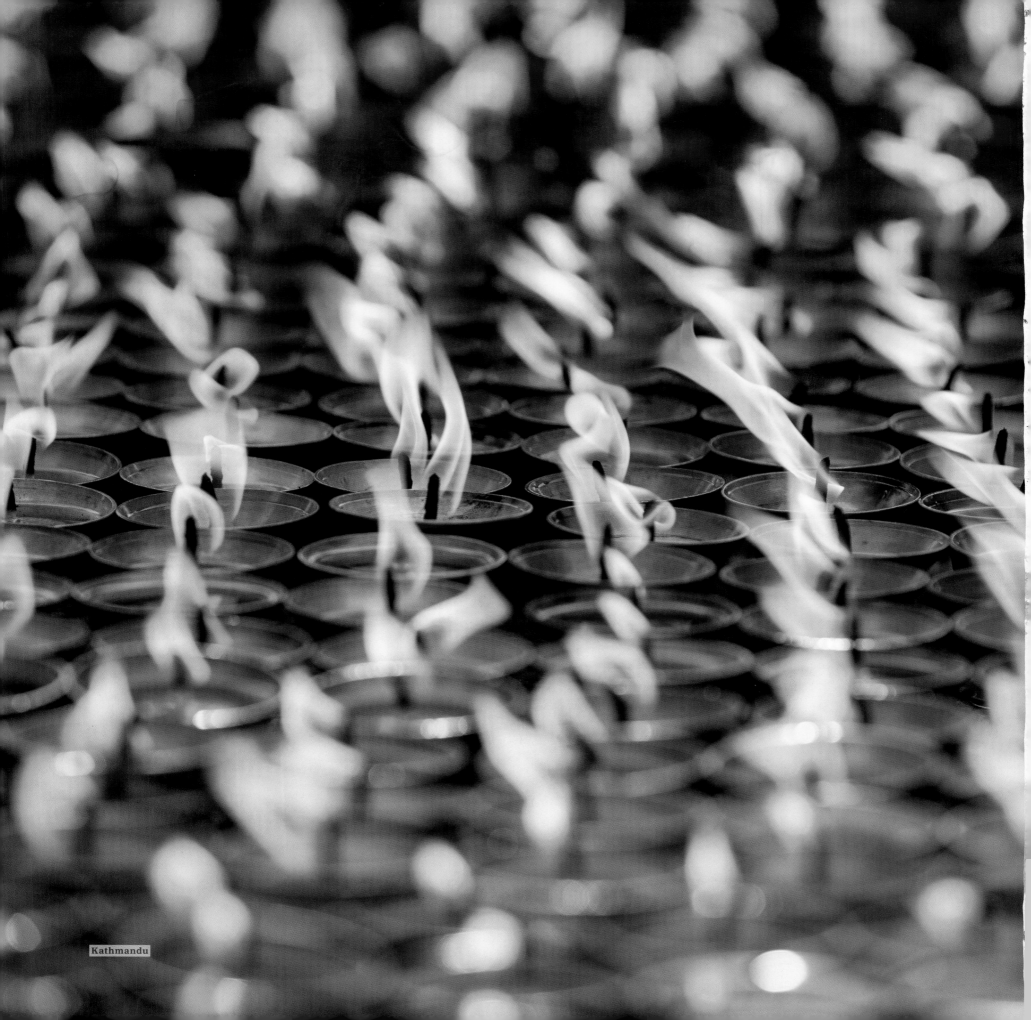
Kathmandu

About Above + Beyond Cancer

Above + Beyond Cancer is a public non-profit organization dedicated to elevating the lives of those touched by cancer. We believe that a cancer diagnosis can be an opportunity for positive change, with an emphasis on health, healing and purpose. Founded in 2011 by oncologist Dr. Richard L. Deming, Above + Beyond Cancer offers innovative programs for cancer survivors based on learning that transforms mind, body and spirit.

In the early years, Above + Beyond Cancer focused primarily on leading cancer survivors on treks around the globe. Beginning in 2011, 29 cancer survivors and caregivers hiked together to Mount Everest Base Camp. Above + Beyond Cancer has since taken survivors on challenging journeys to Mount Kilimanjaro, Mount Kailash in Tibet, Machu Picchu and the Rocky Mountains. Above + Beyond Cancer also coordinated a relay run, Coast-to-Coast for Cancer, from the Pacific Ocean to the Atlantic Ocean, with 160 runners running 4,000 miles. They also competed in the Race Across America (RAAM) with an 8-member team, completing the 3,000 mile race in 6 days, 21 hours and 17 minutes.

Today, Above + Beyond Cancer still leads cancer survivors and caregivers on challenging and transformative journeys to destinations around the world. Each of the journeys also includes a medical/humanitarian element, where survivors spend time at local public hospitals and clinics that serve vulnerable populations within the country they visit.

In addition to worldly adventures, Above + Beyond Cancer also provides cancer survivorship programming to patients and their families in central Iowa throughout the year. In partnership with the YMCA and the MercyOne Health and Fitness Center, we provide weekly educational seminars, indoor studio cycling, yoga, resistance training, and cross training, mindfulness meditation, art classes, cooking and nutrition classes, and a book club. The Adventure Fitness Program challenges cancer survivors to enjoy the benefits of outdoor exercise as well, with camping trips, snowshoeing treks, wilderness hikes, canoeing trips and bicycle rides throughout the year.

Above + Beyond Cancer's weekly Cancer Education Series features experts on topics including cancer treatment, nutrition, healthy lifestyle, cancer prevention, cancer screening, and integrative medicine techniques.

A cancer survivor is defined as anyone who has been diagnosed with cancer regardless of whether they are just starting treatment, have completed treatment or have incurable cancer. Above + Beyond Cancer is proud to partner with all cancer centers in central Iowa to provide services free of charge to survivors and family members. As Justin Anderson, a cancer survivor and member of the first journey to Mount Everest said, "I want people to know that a cancer diagnosis does not have to be the end of your world."

Colorado

About the Drake Community Press

A unique, small-press publisher since 2011, the Drake Community Press is a two-year publishing laboratory that works with non-profit community partners whose compelling mission inspires our student and faculty collaborators. Our motto "Writing *with*" emphasizes a publishing model in which all campus and community stakeholders serve as contributors with a crucial voice in the production process, from inspiration and research to content production to design, marketing and distribution. In our model, we are all students in some form, teachers in another, negotiating across boundaries of campus and community, academic role and disciplines and cultural backgrounds towards a common goal. We share the purpose of producing beautifully designed, thoughtfully written and carefully researched publications on topics of concern to Iowans and to readers far and wide. A variety of individual and corporate funders generously support our goal of community betterment. Proceeds from the sale of our titles support the organizations with whom we partner. If you are interested in supporting the Press through your involvement or with a donation, you can find out more at:

Website - www.drakecommunitypress.org
Email - CommunityPress@drake.edu
Facebook, Instagram, Twitter - @DUCommPress

Carol Spaulding-Kruse
John Fender
Publishers

Kathmandu

Funding

This book was made possible by generous funding from the following:

$10,000 +
W. T. and Edna M. Dahl Trust
Richard L. Deming, M.D.
Drake Center for the Humanities
Fred & Charlotte Hubbell Family
   Charitable Fund
G. David Hurd & Trudy Holman Hurd Fund
Douglas and Deborah West

$5,000 - $9,999
Mike Simonson - Given in memory of
   Charlie Cutler
Cynthia Thorland & Fritz Weitz
   Charitable Fund

$2,500 - $4,999
Medicap, Inc.

$1000 - $2499
Drake College of Arts & Sciences
Drake Office of the Provost

Additional Donors
Brendon and Christine Comito
Chris and Dawn Goodale
Elliott and Kay Smith
Carol Spaulding-Kruse

Participants

DCP Planning Council (2018-2020)

John Amato
  Director of Development, Drake University
Brad Anderson
  Above + Beyond Cancer (2018)
Barbara Boose
  Des Moines University
Dr. Judith Conlin (retired)
  Iowa International Center
Carlyn Crowe
  Drake University School of Journalism
  and Mass Communication
Dr. Richard Deming
  Above + Beyond Cancer
John Fender
  Drake University, Department of
  Art & Design
Claudia Frazer
  Drake University, Cowles Library
Chris Goodale
  Above + Beyond Cancer
Dylan Huey
  Above + Beyond Cancer
Aaron Jaco
  Drake Marketing & Communications
  (2018)
Jan Kaiser
  Kick Marketing
Yasmina Madden
  Drake University, Department of English

Kelsey Parker
  Above + Beyond Cancer
Meredith Ponder
  Drake University Marketing
Kathleen Richardson
  Drake University, School of Journalism
  and Mass Communication
Renee Sedlacek
  Drake University, Center for Engaged
  Learning
Greg Shireman
  Above + Beyond Cancer
Kay Smith
  Des Moines Writers Workshop
Carol Spaulding-Kruse
  Drake Community Press
Mary Van Heukelom
  Above + Beyond Cancer

Editorial Interns (2018-2020)

Madelyn Bjork
Madeline Cheek
Mackenzie Ekern
Annie Howard
Graham Johnson
Jack Kasra
Hannah Nuss
Hallie O'Neill
Kasey Springsteen

Participants

Administrative Evil, Fall 2018
Dr. Lyndi Buckingham-Schutt, Associate Director of Wellness and Nutrition Policy, Harkin Institute
Dr. Allen Zagoren, Associate Professor of Practice and Department Chair, Public Administration

Krystal Kruse
Peter McLaughlin
Jason Mason
Chris Roling
Savannah Wadsworth

Oral Histories and Life Narratives, Fall 2018
Yasmina Madden, Assistant Professor of English
Dr. Sandra Patton-Imani, Professor of Culture and Society

Gabe Altenbernd
Justin Bohnsack
Emilyn Crabbe
Ren Culliney
Jenny English
D'Azhane Felder-Johnson
Allison Kaefring
Avery Malinski
Robyn Michalec
Michael Nestor
Sharyn O'Connor
Steven Peralta Cornejo
Ethan Quick
Kelsey Rick
Zak Risken
Abdullahi Salim
Miranda Strelecki
Helen Trisko
Danni WebbMausbach
Emily Wilson

Strategic Message Design, Fall 2018
Sandy Henry, Professor of Journalism and Mass Communication

Paula Aguirre Gurruchaga
Josie Carrabine
Robert Clark
Jenna Cornick
Hannah Olson
Brett Rosengren
Grace Schofield
Connor Toedtli

Community Writing, Spring 2019
Dr. Carol Spaulding-Kruse, Professor of English

Ren Culliney
Mackenzie Ekern
Ashley Flaws
Cole Friedman
Adam Hathaway
Annie Howard
Jack Kasra
Hallie Keiper
Lauren Lundy
Marisa Morris
Hannah Nuss
Morgan Pattermann
Bryan Solberg

Hope and Optimism, Spring 2019
Dr. Martin Roth, Associate Professor of Philosophy

Danny Berg
Brittany Freeman
Rachel Fritz
Chancelor Halpin
Jeanna Hertaus
Megan Johnson
Clara Kelley
Deanna Krikorian
Julia McGuire
Blake Magill
Hagan Maurer
Will Nurre
Ellie Reter
Kelsey Rick
Seth Strahan
Jacob Sussland
Kristin Thompson
Jessica Vinaja
Nolan Wright
Yifan Zhou

Advanced Typography, Fall 2019
John Fender, Associate Professor of Art and Design

Hunter Beyer
Javairian Estell
Madison Frey
Sophia Gray
Zoe Hanna
Lila Johnson
Emma Kerr
Ashley Wildman

First Year Seminar: Power to the People (and Good Design), Fall 2019
Emily Newman, Assistant Professor of Art and Design

Parker Althaus
Drake Bennett
Brenden Burton
Ava Courneya
Chris Hallum
Mackenzie Hester
Tyler Johnston
Kayla Jones
Emilia Macedo
Abby Marting
Madeline Mews
A.J. Norungolo
Jake Pawlowski
James Phillips
Tanner Pollock
Kelsey Resa
Nathan Specht
Abigail Stumpner
Dylan Valley
Alek Van Eeuwen

Health Sciences Capstone Experience, Fall 2019
Dr. Cassity Gutierrez, College of Pharmacy and Health Sciences
Dr. Alisa Drapeaux, College of Pharmacy and Health Sciences

Alex Peake

Medical Sociology, Fall 2019
Dr. Andrea Kjos, Assistant Professor of Social and Administrative Pharmacy

Elizabeth Aho
Jacob Bennett
Kyle Cass
Annabelle Costanzo
Konstantia Dickens
Laura Harris
Kaitlyn Hester
Annie Howard
Liqin Huang
Stephanie Jarecki
Elena Johanek
Kelly Kroc
Lauren Lerner
Madison Magee
Farhiyo Matan
Carson Reichardt
Nicholas Sickels
Zola Sloth
Rachel Stafford
McKenzie Temperly

Contributors

Survivors and Caregivers

Teresa Adams-
 Tomka
Bikal Adhikari
Sanja Agic-Hajric
Judith Allen
Alicia Anderson
Justin Anderson
Ruth Bachman
Dave Bartemes
Tammy Blaede
Msgr. Frank
 Bognanno
Vicki Bott
Jo Kay Boyle
Michael Brick
Rebecca Christian
 Patience
Amy Colton
Michael Cuesta
Charlie Cutler
Jake Dehaai
Leah Dietrich
Kelly Donato
Dana Downing
Connie Duinink
Dr. Leah Ecklund
Cyndi Elias

Michelle Flattery
Andy Fleming
Julie Goodale
Mary Gottschalk
Richard Graves
Cassity Gutierrez
Julie Hamilton
Diane Hammond
Karla Hansen
Linda Hoskins
Dylan Huey
Laurel Jeffries
Dianne Jones
Jeanna Jones
Trace Kendig
Melisa Klimaszewski
Krystal Kruse
Kelly Lamb
John LaPrairie
Mary LaPrairie
Jeff Lawrence
Suzanne Link
Joni Livermore
Dr. Charlie Lozier
Bev Lund
Yasmina Madden
Kristi Meyer

Sue Mixdorf
Cyndi Mortenson
Dr. Jeff Nichols
Scott Olmstead
Frank Owens
Karen Parman
Debra Peckumn
Steve Reblensky
Christopher Roling
Seán Rose
Joseph Sabroski
Kelly Schall
Sarah Selinger
Jasmine Simpson
Stefanie Stenberg
Kristin Sumbot
Cindy Torvik
Brian Triplett
Miriam Tyson
Mary Van
 Heukelom
Marilyn Vaughan
Kathy Williams
Charlie Wittmack
Tomoko Yajima
Kent Zimmerman
Michael Zimmerman

Acknowledgments

Most of the excerpts in this book were culled from writings by participants on Above + Beyond Cancer journeys undertaken between 2012 and 2018. We owe a huge debt of gratitude to Yasmina Madden who for many years has traveled with A+BC, coached participants who were willing to share their stories and helped to edit, compile and present their work.

Special Thanks

Susie Anderson
  Administrative Assistant, Mercy One
  Cancer Center
Barbara Boose
  Drake Community Press Planning Council
Margaret Corkrean
  Administrative Assistant, College of
  Arts and Sciences
Mary Gottschalk
  Drake Community Press Financial Manager
Doug Lampe
  Senior Advancement Officer, Drake University
Drake University Office of Community
  Engaged Learning
Greg Fuqua
  Adjunct Instructor, Department of
  Art and Design
Lorenzo Sandoval, Iowa Shakespearience
Dr. Chris Snider
  Associate Professor of Journalism and
  Mass Communication
Sofia Turnbull
  Administrative Assistant, Drake University
  Department of English

Acknowledgments

Works Cited

Agnew, Lois. "Ecologies of Cancer Rhetoric: The Shifting Terrain of US Cancer Wars, 1920-1980." College English, vol. 80, no. 3, 2018, 271-96.

Anderson, Justin. Take a Hike Justin: A Blog Mostly About My Cancer Journey. WordPress, takeahikejustin.com, 2020.

Armstrong, Lance. *It's Not About the Bike: My Journey Back to Life.* New York, The Berkley Publishing Group, 2000.

Bono. "2008 Women's Conference Speech." Women's Conference, 22 Oct. 2008, Long Beach Convention Center, Long Beach, CA. Guest Speech.

Cancer Disparities: A Chartbook. Washington, D.C., American Cancer Society Action Network, 2018.

Chodron, Pema. *When Things Fall Apart: Heart Advice for Difficult Times.* Boulder, Shambhala Publications, Inc., 1997.

Cousineau, Phil. *The Art of Pilgrimage: The Seeker's Guide to Making Travel Sacred.* San Francisco, Conari Press, 1998.

Dalai Lama, Desmond Tutu, and Douglas Abrams. *The Book of Joy: Lasting Happiness in a Changing World.* New York, Avery, 2016.

@DrMayaAngelou. "This is a wonderful day. I've never seen this one before." Twitter, 17 May 2013, 1:44 p.m., https://twitter.com/drmayaangelou/status/335465952969900032?lang=en.

Ehrmann, Max. "Desiderata." 1927. All Poetry, https://allpoetry.com/Desiderata---Words-for-Life. Accessed 12 Feb. 2020.

Emmons, RA and ME McCullough. "Counting Blessings Versus Burdens: An Experimental Investigation of Gratitude and Subjective Well-Being in Daily Life." *Journal of Personality and Social Psychology,* vol. 84, no. 2, 2003, pp. 377-389.

Ensler, Eve. *In the Body of the World: A Memoir.* New York, Metropolitan Books, 2013.

Esposito, Lisa. "13 Ways Social Determinants Affect Health." U.S. News, 29 Nov. 2017, https://health.usnews.com/health-care/patient-advice/slideshows/13-ways-social-determinants-affect-health.

Frank, Arthur. *The Wounded Storyteller: Body, Illness, and Ethics.* Chicago, University of Chicago Press, 1995.

Frankl, Victor. *Man's Search for Meaning.* Boston, Beacon Press, 2006.

Gawande, Atul. *Being Mortal.* New York, Metropolitan Books, 2014.

Halifax, Joan. *Being with Dying: Cultivating Compassion and Fearlessness in the Presence of Death.* Boston, Shambhala Publications, 2008.

Kübler-Ross, Elizabeth and David Kessler. *On Grief and Grieving: Finding the Meaning of Grief Through the Five Stages of Loss.* New York, Simon & Schuster, Inc., 2014.

Kushner, Harold. "God's Fingerprints on the Soul." *Handbook for the Soul,* edited by Richard Carlson and Benjamin Shield, Little, Brown and Company, 1995.

McGeer, Victoria. "The Art of Good Hope." *The Annals of the American Academy of Political and Social Science,* vol. 592, no. 1, pp. 100-27.

Acknowledgments

Machado, Antonio. "Proverbios y Cantares." *Fields of Castile/Campos de Castilla: A Dual Language Book.* Translated by Stanley Appelbaum, Dover Publications, Inc., 2007.

Maslow, Abraham. Abraham Maslow Collection. HPA Mss 23. Department of Special Collections, Davidson Library, University of California, Santa Barbara.

Mukherjee, Siddhartha. *The Emperor of All Maladies: A Biography of Cancer.* New York, Scribner, 2010.

O'Donohue, John. "For Courage." *To Bless the Space Between Us.* New York, Random House, Inc., 2008.

Oliver, Mary. "The Summer Day." *New and Selected Poems,* Volume One. Boston, Beacon Press, 1992.

Stegner, Wallace. *All the Little Live Things.* New York, The Penguin Group, 1967.

Womack, Lee Ann. "I Hope You Dance." *I Hope You Dance,* MCA Nashville, 2000.

Used with Permission of the Author
Charlie Cutler speech–20 June 2015, Prairie Meadows Ballroom, Altoona, IA
Justin Anderson blog "Take a Hike"
Rebecca Christian Patience (personal essay)

Disclaimer
We have endeavored to represent the work of dozens of participants and to include the voices of a great many contributors in this two-year, multi-faceted project. Our goal has been 100% accuracy. We sincerely regret any instance that falls short of that goal.

Editor's Note
For medical terminology, we have followed the style guidelines of the American Medical Association. In the rare instances when the choice arises, we have chosen to employ the plural pronoun *they* with reference to singular nouns.

Photography
All photos by Dylan Huey unless noted

Colophon
This book was designed by Drake University Department of Art and Design students enrolled in Advanced Typography in the fall of 2019 under the direction of John Fender. The type is set in Open Sans, designed by Steve Matteson, and IBM Plex Serif, designed by Mike Abbink in collaboration with Bold Monday. This edition is printed on Hansol Titan Dull, 80 lb. text paper by Sigler in Ames, Iowa.